D0893802

The Saint of the Atom Bomb

The Saint o

ne Atom Bomb

by Josef Schilliger

Translated from the German by David Heimann

The Newman Press • Westminster, Maryland

1955

Contents

The Saint of the Atom Bomb

I

The Long Seconds

A miniature city arose on a rectangular block of stone in New Mexico. It was like a giant bunker on the mountainside, like a medieval fortress with its towers, like a peaceful monastery behind its walls. A great mystery was kept hidden here in a closely guarded sanctuary behind four rings of protecting walls.

The outermost ring consisted, to the west and east, of the Jemez Mountain Range, rising to four thousand feet, and the Sangre de Christo Chain. The steep precipices of the Canons guarded the location to the north and south. The outer circle was the "city wall." It consisted of a

3

high, wide-meshed wire fence, connected to an alarm system by photo-electric cells, and it twinkled in the evening with hundreds of tiny lights, each no bigger than the head of a pin.

The inner ring of defense was made up by the 1000 police who were in charge of the 10,000 inhabitants. They looked at every visitor's pass with suspicion, fenced off infected streets and areas, censored all telephone conversations and all of the mail. Individual buildings, even individual rooms, were under their constant observation, and they even knew the private conversations held in this modern city. In the innermost circle, the professional secrets of the chemists and physicists were enveloped in complete security. A gentle "Shhhhh" was enough to cut off every question from an inquisitive wife.

This was Los Alamos, New Mexico, in 1945.

* * *

Black scraps of cloud chased along above the barren stones outside the city. The rain thudded down into the gloomy sand. Lightning flashed

4

through the night with a pale glow and illuminated a tall and lonely tower. The rolling thunder which followed echoed eerily off the lofty mountain peaks. The atomic research scientist, Dr. Oppenheimer, had been crawling out of the dugout with General Groves every quarter hour since one o'clock in the morning to look at the sky. Anxiously they squinted in the direction of the tower, six miles away. It was 3:30 when they decided: "At 5:30 we can fire."

Now a portable radio transmitter was put into operation. At long, irregular intervals it interrupted the silence of the desert: "4:00: the rain has stopped!—4:30: the sky is starting to clear! —5:00: the explosion will follow in thirty minutes!"

A great hour in the history of the world had dawned, an hour that would mark the birth of a new era. These were long seconds for the three hundred scholars and the Nobel Prize winners assembled for the event. In suspense and paralyzing anxiety they awaited a new "creation"—perhaps the beginning of the destruction of the world;

5

peace for millions—probably death for hundreds of thousands.

Out there on the sandy desert floor the ripe fruit of atomic science rested on the platform of a steel tower. Two billion dollars, a row of newly built cities, long years of research, the sweat of 100,000 workers—all were out there, with the plutonium. Five hundred miles of cable connected the bomb with the hundred control instruments of the observation posts. Specially equipped B-29 superfortresses had taken off to record the effects of the explosion at the highest altitudes. The heaviest tanks were drawn up along the danger line; their built-in seismographs were to register the earthquake.

In his dugout of mud and wood, Dr. Oppenheimer adjusted the levers and controls of his apparatus for the last time. Now he searched for a small wooden prop; now he stared for minutes into the distance. He was about to see the forces of hell bubbling up before him. Distractedly he listened to the radio announcer: "Minus 20 minutes . . . minus 15 minutes!" The minutes seemed like creeping eternities. Of the 20 physicists near Dr. Oppenheimer one young assistant could stand it no longer. He left to find a safer place to hide.

Out there near the explosion tower an unsuspecting herd of antelope was feeding and sniffing at the meager sagebrush. A few desert jackrabbits scurried from their path.

"Minus 10 minutes . . . minus 5!"

Stammered prayers were on the lips of the scientists at all the control points in these last moments. As if by command, they threw themselves flat on the dusty ground, face down, eyes pressed into the crook of their arms, their feet pointed in the direction of the steel tower.

"Minus 3 minutes . . . minus 2!"

Excitement was mounting to the bursting point. Hardly a breath could be heard. A deep silence crept over the scene, interrupted only by fervent prayers.

The last seconds! They were more difficult to bear than the front lines under heavy bombardment. At the signal "45 seconds" the robot mechanism in the tower grasped the bomb and guided it without human aid.

* * *

"Now!"

A flash of purple and gold and violet and gray quivered over the desert wastes of New Mexico. Every crevice, every gorge, even the long extinguished craters of the most distant mountain peaks were illuminated in the light of ten suns. It was majestic, indescribably beautiful!

A mountain of cloud towered up in the morning sky, 40,000 feet high. First it was a dancing globe, then a giant mushroom; soon it was a flaming column.

After thirty seconds a roaring wind swept through the sand dunes, whirling by at 600 miles an hour, ten times faster than a hurricane. A long drawn out thunder chased after it, swelling and ebbing until it broke on the four thousand foot mountains of the nearby range, and howled through the desert loneliness like an awful echo of Judgment Day.

The steel tower with the apparatus had gone up in smoke and a yawning crater had been rent in the wilderness, like a door to the underworld. The sand hills had melted into green glass, and the antelope had disappeared. Not a rattlesnake, not a desert jackrabbit, not a branch of sagebrush was left. In the dugouts the scientists rolled over on their sides and blinked through darkened glasses at the sparkling mountain of fire. Now they groped their way to their feet, drawn and tired, wiping the dust from their clothes. Completely shaken, they had lost the gift of speech; reverently, as in prayer, they marveled at the power of nature.

"Fire and heat, praise the Lord!—Lightning and clouds, praise the Lord!" Everybody was thinking what General Farrel later put into words: "We felt that we tiny creatures were being blas-

9

phemous in daring to set in motion the powers that until then had been reserved to the Almighty."

Everyone felt bound, as under a solemn vow, to pledge his whole life so that the power just set free would be used always for good, never for evil.

Suddenly Dr. Oppenheimer was surrounded and congratulated from all sides, lifted in the air by almost a dozen arms. Loud cries of triumph resounded in the morning, and the long pent up excitement gave vent to a wild burst of enthusiasm and prolonged handshaking.

The test was successful; it had surprised even the greatest optimists. Science had gone beyond the elements; the atom bomb, after long years, was finally born.

* * *

High in the southwest corner of the State of Washington there was a row of gloomy gray sand-hills. Dusty bushes of gray-green sagebrush lined a dried-up river bed. The mighty Columbia River thundered through the rolling tableland westwards. Metal smokestacks, camouflaged in gray, stretched into the misty horizon, looking from a distance like thin lead pencils. Windowless blocks of concrete towered up out of the sand into rectangular fortresses. Along the broad smooth highways stood a row of warning placards with black circles. A column of heavily armed watch towers, 450 yards apart, encircled this restricted area of more than three thousand square feet.

This was the Hanford Engineering Works of Richland, the first plant in the world for the development of atomic energy. Here in this inland desert, thirty miles away from every sign of human habitation, a giant chemical laboratory was built. It required as much cement as a concrete road from Chicago to St. Louis. The magnetic coils for the plant's own electrical works took fourteen tons of silver alone. In June of 1944, 45,000 workmen were busy on its construction.

"Danger! Tighten your masks! Don't forget your gloves! Hold your breath! Stay out!" That was the welcome from a hundred signs and placards. In the bare, bunker-like halls a unique and clever warning system had been installed. "Attention! Alpha Rays! They get into your hair and clothing down to the skin! Caution! Beta Rays! They bore right under the skin! Be on your guard! Gamma Rays! They eat their way into your body!" The automatic, highly sensitive speaker systems continually screamed from the walls.

Every half hour the guard personnel, muffled and masked, would come with Geiger counters to examine all the tables and switch boards for harmful radiation. Workmen dressed like divers in their tank equipment shuffled by with yard-long tools to carefully remove a poisoned screw or rod. Busy doctors, known as "guardian angels," acted as the health guards for the Hanford Works. They passed through the clean and the infected zones, through the "cold" as well as through the "hot" sections. Doors opened before them automatically.

Every group of four workers had an "angel" who met them several times in the course of each day. He took them by the hand and checked their pulses, examined their thyroid glands, and kept an individual record book for each of his charges.

"Here is your pin with the radioactive sensitive film! Here is your ring with the tester compound. And don't forget the Hanford chemical reactor. If it changes from green to yellow, it means just average danger. Orange means extreme danger." This was how each worker was received every morning by the watchman at the factory door. They put their lunches into a radiation-proof steel cabinet at the canteen and then changed their clothes. From steel lockers they took fresh underclothes, then wrapped and muffled themselves in three inches of rubber boots and gloves, protective glasses and helmets.

Next they shuffled out of the "clean" zone into the middle, or "disinfection" zone, passing on their way other workmen who were getting ready to leave, foaming with soap. Then, through automatically opening doors, they made their way into the "hot" zone. An "angel" waited for them in the windowless hall; the foreman would hand a logbook to the leader which contained instructions on work for the day. Finally the men stood for hours at a high black wall full of dials and gauges, pressing a button from time to time, turning a wheel, adjusting a lever.

Meanwhile, invisible behind a wall a yard thick, seethed an absolute hell of radioactive materials, and through great canals the cool water of the Columbia River thundered over the furnaces, enough each day to supply the needs of an average city.

Suddenly the loudspeakers crackled and groaned. The bare walls of the compartments flung the echo through the entire plant. One of the atomic furnaces was no longer functioning.

A swarm of mummy-like figures bobbed up with

gas masks and the "guardian angels" crowded around them. Without any personal contact, they set about operating on the ailing giant. A robot with an uncanny sense of touch went to work. This long steel "limb" was capable of performing the seven fundamental motions of the human hand. From a distance of 100 yards, behind the thick walls, it responded to commands, located the proper screws, unscrewed them, and put others in their place.

The sirens went on. The burner began working again, and the section of the machine that had had to be replaced was carried to the "cemetery." The "cemeteries" were gloomy squares out in the wasteland, surrounded by cement posts painted in red. Here the radioactive scraps were buried in deep graves. Muffled "cemetery guards" kept watch each day over an area of 120 miles; they sent bleating flocks of sheep as "plutonium tasters" above the graves that would still be sending out their poisonous rays after thousands of years.

What was happening in this giant laboratory out

there in the desert? The Hanford burners were producing fissionable plutonium from uranium ore. Uranium atoms crack in an explosion in ten-millionths of a second and produce an energy of 55 billion degrees Celsius. This heat is three times greater than that in the innermost heart of the sun, and the force of the explosion is ten million times stronger than dynamite. One bomb, properly used, would be able to lift the whole American navy ten thousand feet into the air and cause a hurricane of more than 600 miles per hour.

Here in the silent wilderness of Richland the researchers were conjuring up a new element at their beck and call. For the first time in history human hands were able to uncover elements hidden until now. Plutonium, more precious than gold, is the offspring of neptunium and the grandson of uranium. In the utmost quiet behind the instruments and dials, regulated by an automatic clock mechanism, great prodigies of nature were taking place.

With the airplane, telephone, and radio, space and time have been overcome; with atomic energy, nature herself, the whole world. Now, at his will, man can simply wipe out whole sections of the earth from the glory of creation's morning.

II

The Peaceful City on the Blue Bay

The atomic project set loose a migration of nations in New Mexico. Residential towns disappeared, and atomic cities sprang up over night on the desert sands. In comical processions of giant trucks the architects moved whole houses away from the accursed atom land. Laborers would take even the dead from their graves, lay them in coffins of fresh pine, and flee northward with them, away from the omnipotence of the atom. This was the triumph of a century, the victory of the atom. The dead must flee, to give birth to other dead.

On four unplaned pine boards at the entrance of one of these cities dedicated to the dead, there is a sign written in large letters: "It is hard to understand why our city had to be destroyed, just to make a bomb which will destroy the city of someone else—a city which he loved as much as we loved ours. . . ." Another such city was Nagasaki.

*　*　*

"Ashita hamabe ni samayo-eba. . . . In the morning, when I go walking by the sea shore . . ." A breeze, fresh from the sea, had lifted the pleasant melody of this folk song upon its wings and carried it from the city park along the tiny workers' houses of the old city. The long-necked shamis sent their choleric "klimp-pling, klimp-pling" through the heavy paper windows with every gust of air. The sanguine bamboo flutes sang out in high spirits, inviting everyone, "Come, the festival has begun!"

It was the end of March or the first days of April. The cherry trees along the quay had been in

19

bloom for three days, their branches spreading a roof of glistening rosy blossoms for the joyous crowds of the festival. The ocean bay, half a mile wide, was painted a deep, shimmering blue in the reflection of the spring sun.

The Geishas came tripping daintily out of the cover of a narrow, shadowy lane. With infinite patience, in front of their mirrors, they had done up their jet black hair into a gay little tower. Farther down along the sea they were already swinging back and forth in the delicate gestures of the Geisha dance. The small, bald-headed Japanese men were goaded on by the sweet sake, and for the duration of the festival they laid aside the wrinkled nervous mien of their business life. Their bashful wives followed them in their colorful butterfly-kimonos, carrying wooden food chests full of special delicacies made from recipes of rice and crayfish. Half of the city was streaming into the gala hall beneath the canopy of blossoms in the park.

Nagasaki was celebrating her cherry blossom

festival, a festival of joy and peace. Nagasaki! Where did she get her ringing name? Didn't she once, with the innocent look of a juggler on her face, steal into paradise, and smuggle a little parcel of undisturbed peace into Kyushu, the southernmost of the four islands of the empire? Yes, but she was not completely secure in her thievery, and with a crafty smile she hid herself behind a chain of watchtowers and lighthouses, behind a wall of shielding islands. In the deep blue water of the warm Tsushim Gulf they were baptized on creation's morning, and given the resounding names "Enoshima, Amakusa, Naga-shima."

It is small wonder that in the sixteenth and seventeenth centuries the Italian, Spanish, and Portuguese missionaries found once more in the fishing village of Nagasaki the happy sun they had known in their own far off countries. In the budding beauty of the subtropical climate they learned to laugh and joke once again, to fight against the melancholy that so often accompanied their services in the care of souls.

21

It was and is the lot of the Catholic priests of the Oura-Tenshudo Church in Nagasaki to skim along the dark blue fiords in their boats, past the ever green peninsulas, threading their way toward one of the islands amid the morning song of the wild canary birds, preparing for a "Sermon on the Mount." It was and is their duty to wander in shirt-sleeves along a pathless country through fields of red azaleas, bringing the Blessed Sacrament into the straw-roofed huts that house the descendants of the Kirishitan Catholics. "Ye mountains and hills, ye seas and lakes, praise the Lord," they can murmur over and over again.

Nagasaki was and remains a holy city, a place of pilgrimage. Even now a young girl, her eyes red with weeping beneath the fringe of her characteristically bobbed hair, slipped through the paper doors of the little parsonage. She choked and sobbed and told the priest the story of her life, then went into the city to stay a day or two in the holy place.

The grace of the pilgrimage, the sun of Kyushu,

and the kindliness of the missionaries and the Sisters shone down upon her for a while, and then she left for home with a brighter smile. In the magnificent splendor of Nagasaki, she had completely forgotten that she had ever despaired, or that she had once wanted to hurl herself from an outjutting crag into the dark blue floods of Omura Bay.

Daily there were hundreds of pilgrims. They squeezed in weary procession through the steep and narrow lanes to climb praying and singing up the low martyrs' hill, the Tateyama, in the middle of the city. At the foot of the hill they would throw themselves on the well-worn mats in the cemetery church and pray to the arch-martyrs. "You holy ambassadors of our island! Do not forget us; represent us well at the Court of Heaven!"

Then they mounted the winding path to the shining red brick cathedral where the pastor of Urakami entered for the Solemn High Mass as the Cardinal and Primate of East Asia. This

23

church, which seats 6000, is the largest cathedral in Eastern Asia.

Finally the pilgrimage wound its way toward the episcopal church of Oura-Tenshudo, the first European construction on Kyushu and a national treasure of Japan. Proud palm trees, like sentinels standing on parade, lined both sides of the long, high steps which led the pilgrims into the mystic half-shadow of the church. With elegant Oriental hospitality a native priest received them and conducted them to the Madonna shrine. A subdued sunbeam stole through the blue window and flooded the statue under the Gothic pointed arch with a pale light, in sharp contrast to the dusky church.

* * *

After a profoundly deep bow of homage which seemed to contain all the gravity and reverence of the entire Orient, the priestly leader began to speak: "Turn back the time eighty years to the past. During those days the priests were under a ban, and this sanctuary was built and consecrated under the protection of the French embassy. A month later, on Friday afternoon, March 17, 1865, the Franciscan missionary, Father Petitjean, came upon a group of twelve men, women, and children. One man, holding a rain cap shiny with oil in his hand, greeted the missionary with measured respect and as an interpreter for the group, began, 'All of us here have the same heart as you.'

" 'Indeed!' responded the missionary from Paris, 'but where are you from?'

" 'Urakami; and in Urakami almost everyone has the same heart as you.'

"A woman stepped up from the background. Simply and reverently she too bowed her head and begged, 'Santa Maria no gozowa doko?' ('Where is the statue of the Blessed Virgin?') With a broad, fatherly gesture the missionary led the group inside to the niche of the Madonna.

" 'Santa Maria,' one voice intoned. 'Santa Maria,' the others repeated, all in refrain, high voices and deep, singly and together. They concluded

25

with this new Magnificat: 'On ko Jesus Sama—Jesus Sama!' ('Just look at Jesus, the Son of God, in her arms!').

"Suddenly Peter Domingo, who had spoken for them, the man with the pigtail wrapped in a spiral at the back of his head as if for a festival, approached Father Petitjean and stammered, 'But don't you have any children?'

" 'You and all your brothers from all of Japan are the children that God has given us,' the Father consoled them. 'Just like your first missionaries, the priest must live without marrying his entire life.'

" 'O Arigato!' ('Thanks be to God!') escaped from Peter Domingo's lips. 'O Arigato!' They all took it up and showed their happiness by deep bows, bending as far as the floor. Then they added, as if in explanation, 'Virgen degozaru' ('They are not married'). Filled with joy, these twelve early Christians hurried out in their fishing boats across to the islands and up to the peasants' huts with the pointed straw roofs.

26

"The news quickly spread from one to another. 'Just think! After 250 years a Catholic priest is once more among us!' Soon the 15,000 Christians in Nagasaki and the surrounding country knew about it. A solemn delegation received Father Petitjean like a prince with the cry 'Mia Sama,' and carried him up into the mountains to the sanctuary of their hidden baptisms, prayers, and sermons under the protecting roof of the trees."

* * *

With eager ears, and for the most part with eyes wide open, and not infrequently with gaping mouths, the pilgrims listened to this singular example of Church history where laymen passed along their faith for centuries without priests.

Deeply moved, they cast themselves down on the holy ground of Nagasaki before the "Regina Japoniae," ("Queen of Japan"), and softly murmured the evening prayer of the pilgrimage.

The pilgrims happily removed their dusty grey "getas" in the terrace-like "engawa" and exchanged them for slippers to walk softly and

27

easily over the "tatamis" on the floor of the pilgrimage house. Soon they were stretched out on their padded quilts over the floor. The breeze, fresh from the sea, helped to ease them into a peaceful sleep. The scrolls covered with writing swayed back and forth along the wall, and the cut branches heavy with blossom stirred gently in the painted vases.

III

The Seeker after Peace

Three weak silver notes glided timidly over the cornice of the tower window. Then the Angelus bell of the Cathedral of Nagasaki began to swing with full force. Like the spray from a playful mountain waterfall, the chimes rushed out and over the tower. They tumbled through the air, full of life, sprinkling the cathedral hill down toward the university. With holy impatience they beat and pounded on the windowpanes and whispered into the lecture hall, "The Angel of the Lord declared unto Mary."

Every noon for two years the melody from these bells had been ringing in the ears of a tall, 23-

year-old medical student. Takashi Nagai looked up from his lecture notes to the window and stared at the two mighty Cathedral towers. Then his half closed eyes followed the white veiled pilgrims as they stepped from the front door and wound their way down the path. "Ah, the poor slaves of a Western sect!" he remarked to his neighbors.

But today the voice of these bells pounded not only at his ear, but also at his heart. It seemed to linger with him, to follow him the whole day long. He could not shake it off. In the middle of the night the echo rushed in at him again, ". . . declared unto Mary . . . Takashi, declared unto Mary, declared. . . ."

Takashi, the future doctor, spent his youth in Izumo, in the western part of the Island of Honshu, near Hiroshima, on the coast of the Sea of Japan. His father had given up a post as assistant in the women's clinic at Matsue around 1900 to come to Izumo, where he proceeded to build up a country practice. The elder Nagai carefully nursed his many patients back to health, and was regarded at Izumo as an emperor or a god.

At sunset he would generally unbutton his doctor's apron, and, with the help of his wife, putter about at fan-making, happy and content, until nearly midnight. One afternoon each week he would lock up his business and try for spotted trout in the neighboring brook, or strum the triangular guitar with his wife and children. He combined in himself a half dozen official duties and positions and did much to improve the culture of the remote little town.

To this uncrowned noble was born a little prince, Takashi, on January 3, 1908. With four brothers and sisters he grew up carefree, happy, and gay at the romantic country residence in Izumo. His heathen parents used to dispense him regularly from the pilgrimages, ceremonial bathing, and flower offerings of Shintoism.

There was, to be sure, a little corner stand for the gods. But the wooden casket, with all its

31

carved flourishes and the names of the rice god Inani and the sun goddess Amaterasu, was really only an ancient ornamental piece.

"Go ahead to Matsue in the Shintoist procession! Go on and try to touch the sedan chair of the gods as it swings back and forth in your procession!" Takashi would cry arrogantly after his companions. "I prefer to stay in my father's park and amuse myself by watching the little bears turn somersaults behind the trunk of an almond tree."

"Papa! Mama! Why do you work so much? Why don't you lie down to rest with me?" little ten-year-old Takashi wondered one evening, looking thoughtfully over a mountain of books at his mother and father beside a varnished little table.

"Sit down on the straw mat a minute," his father told him; "after all, you're almost grown up now. It's time you knew how your father came to be a doctor. I was a good-for-nothing—yes, a good-for-nothing. School no longer held any interest for me. Finally, at his wit's end, my

32

father, a doctor, sent me to tend sheep and mules on a farm in the farthest corner of Honshu. I ran away. Four long years I was missing. Finally, 21 years old, I returned to my father as a doctor with a diploma. He just sat there, dumb with surprise and joy, and kept turning his glasses over in his hand."

"But, Papa," Takashi interrupted him, "aren't you a real doctor?"

"Just keep on listening, and do as I have done. I worked days for a doctor as receptionist, helped him in his pharmacy and at the operating table, and went with him on house calls. Then at night I was at my books, until I would fall asleep and they would serve me as a hard pillow. . . ."

In the reflection of the heavy oil lamp with the flower-painted shade Takashi's eyes grew large and sparkling that evening. Without a word he left the room with his usual goodnight bow. An ideal had begun to shine in his young soul.

* * *

Father Nagai, 59 years old, lay dead before his children, wasted to a skeleton by cancer. His wife, with the capacity for sacrifice that Japanese mothers have, had given him five little children, had assisted him every day with his patients, and had found a good word to whisper to each along with the medicine. Besides that she did all her housework by herself and found the time to seek out the little straw huts of the poor, never forgetting to smile. Now she was left alone to continue the upbringing of her children.

In 1928 Takashi finished his classical education and, twenty years old, had himself registered in the medical faculty at Nagasaki. It was not long before he dissected his first corpse. Like a living mummy, with a mask on his nose and mouth, he stood beside it. "What I just had in my hands," he philosophized, "was never anything more than pure matter," and with a grand gesture he pulled his gloves from his hands.

Takashi had become a dyed-in-the-wool materialist. He wanted to be an ultra-modern Japanese, and as he described it: "Life lasts only till the grave. Let us drink and sing and dance and play, before the joy of youth is gone."

In the spring of 1930 Takashi completed the second year of his higher studies. Rejoicing under the spring sky he gave himself over without reserve to the celebration of the free days. Then a telegram reached him from Izumo: "Mother has had a stroke." He took the next steamer and hurried to her deathbed.

She was already in her last agony but mustered a last little bit of life together and tried to hold off death. She had something to say to Takashi, a message that only a mother could deliver. He came and threw himself down beside the cotton blanket of her floor-level bed. He closed her wrinkled, crippled hand into him own and bowed his head over hers. . . .

"She fell asleep, her eyes fastened urgently on me. This dying look of my mother completely changed my way of thinking," he had to confess later with tears. "Oh, the dumb look of her that bore and reared me, and loved me up to the end! It told me clearly that her soul would always be at the side of her dear Takashi, even after her death."

*   *   *

"L'homme n'est qu'un roseau, le plus faible de la nature, mais c'est un roseau pensant." "Man is only a reed, the weakest in nature but he is a reed that thinks." Takashi, returning from his mother's burial, was reading Pascal's "Pensées." He stared a moment from the steamer out upon the waves, shook his head, wrapped the book in its cloth cover, and rested his chin on his right hand. What was this Catholic Faith that even the wise Pascal, the discoverer of the binomial theorem, could accept it, without finding anything to contradict his scientific knowledge!

Takashi was on the road to the Catholic Church —but who would show him the path and help him knock upon the gate? He let his eyes roam over the mirrored surface of the sea, and suddenly he saw himself as one who wants to cross a great ocean, without a boat, without a guide.

*   *   *

Every noon the greeting of the Angelus bells continued to pierce the monotony of the lecture hall. Takashi could resist no longer. He decided to get within earshot of the mysterious voice. He went down among the ten thousand Catholics of Urakami. He took a room at the Moriyamas, a family descended directly from the early Christians. Father Moiyama went out every morning to his cattle business, his peaked cap on his bald head. "What! The refined Pascal with his fine French wig did not find it strange to live in the same faith with these uneducated people?" The medical student was shocked. A cattle dealer, by his quiet example, became the tutor of a proud and self-sufficient scholar.

In 1932 Takashi passed the doctor's examination and was celebrating the occasion with a festive tea party. Midori, the daughter of his landlord, was invited. In her holiday kimono, hov-

37

ering about the party, she looked like an angel. Midori knelt with a curtsey on the carpet before the beaming guests and prepared their cups and dishes with dainty gestures. She put on the smile of a saint and handed Takashi a cup for the first swallow, as lovingly and gently as if she were afraid the gold bird on the saucer might fly away from her . . . together with the young Takashi.

Shortly before, the young doctor had taken a severe cold which left him with impaired hearing. As he could no longer use the stethoscope properly on his patients, he decided to specialize in radiology. The X-ray machine was to become his inseparable, life-long friend; finally, it was to become his executioner. At first Dr. Nagai was an unassuming assistant, then a private instructor, and at last head doctor in the X-ray division.

In February of 1933, in the proud uniform of a medical officer, Takashi took part in the Japanese war against Manchuria. Once, under the howl and whistle of the grenades, he crawled up to the front lines, treating and saving several dozen wounded. Takashi received the Imperial Golden

Order of the Eagle for this act of heroism. Midori Moriyama, sending him a service package, enclosed a tiny little book: the catechism. During the long Manchurian winter evenings, under the screeching of the artillery fire, he learned it by heart. Returning to Nagasaki in June of 1934, the future university professor once again became a lowly student. He called on the grey-headed pastor of Urakami, asking to be examined in the Faith, and then had himself baptized. He chose Poro (Paul) as his baptismal name—St. Paul for the patron of his life; St. Paul of whom the Lord said on the day of his baptism, "I shall show him how much he must suffer for my name." Two months later Poro Nagai took Midori for his wife.

* * *

"Poro! What a Croesus your friend Hagashiyama is getting to be!" Mrs. Nagai murmured as she pushed back the paper door of their poor little dwelling. She was just returning from a visit.

"He owns all the fisheries on Goto Island," answered Poro drily.

"That luxurious curved furniture!" Midori Nagai

39

complained. "We'll never manage that," and a little green spark of envy stole into her eyes.

"It wouldn't be right, and it wouldn't be much use either," her husband tried to soothe her. "Hagashiyama is an epicure, and he sponges on his friends. We Christians are supposed to be the servants of our fellow men."

"You're right!" said Midori. "Let's keep it just like that, as long as we live." She set to work at the humming sewing machine. Poro went to the desk that a prisoner at a work camp had built for him cheaply.

At the bottom of the Uramaki River Valley the little house that Poro and Midori had occupied since their marriage required only six mats to cover its floor surface. The red brick cathedral towered up on the hill to one side, and the university on the other. Forty paltry yen a month was all that the assistant could lay before his wife on the low dining room table. But Midori was an artist; she had managed to keep house with that for seven years now. It was never enough for a ticket to the theater, nor for a glass of sake in the restaurant. They could allow themselves a holiday only once each year—a little journey to the sea-shore. Midori herself tailored his clothes with such a skillful hand that the laboratory assistants often teased their professor and remarked: "Why Doctor! Really you must let your wife pamper you all day long!" All day long? But Doctor Nagai was so seldom at home; he would generally sit at his X-ray machine and forget everything else around him.

Dr. Nagai was at home in the laboratory of the university. Here he held sway as a scientist just like a king. A heavy lead apron, a mighty pair of protective glasses, and a pair of leaden gloves made up his royal wardrobe. His subjects were the invisible ultra rays that crackled and hummed, but which were so treacherous and so secretive, seeking after his life. Now he would come in with a box of guinea pigs or mice. Now he would shove a jar of sprouting soy beans or a swarm of drosophila flies behind a glass shade under the radiation machine. He kept his little kingdom carefully locked off from every curious nose and every eager eye, until after long, sleepless nights he could enter a new result in his filing cabinet. Then he would entrench himself behind the bunker of his thick paneling, photograph files, and card indexes.

Dr. Nagai made notes and sketches with the tenacious perseverance of a research expert. In a few short years he would publish ten significant works, and show his colleagues new ways to find and cure treacherous diseases with the X-ray.

Nevertheless the rector of the university said, "The stethoscope is more important than your experiments in radiography." And Professor Asakura added spitefully, "Stop this nonsense and learn something decent!"

Dr. Nagai held his peace and swallowed his pride. He went on with his research and with his hoping. Often he staggered from his study completely exhausted and pale as death.

Meanwhile, as a member of the St. Vincent de Paul Society, he would frequently turn up in the damp little huts of the poor along the shore of the Urami River, where he would dig a warm "mompe" or a pair of "getas" out of his bag for the children. The doctor would be at his desk before dawn, signing his name to the forms that would arrange housing for one or two of the wretchedly poor. Scolding housewives would come barging into his office. He often took his place as a mediator between them. Then, too, he would work as an organizer for a splendid gymnastic festival to be held in the city square. He himself often climbed into his training uniform, and was always a passionate baseball player.

On Saturday evenings, Dr. Nagai would whip off his doctor's apron for just one short day and devote his undivided attention to his wife, his little daughter Kayano, and his little son Makoto. The children always waited for him at the garden gate under the little roof, which was turned up at the ends like a pagoda. There a childish contest would ensue. Whose turn was it to take father's wraps from him, or drag the padded silk quilt

43

before the steaming bath? Poro Nagai was then no longer a doctor, but a father.

He often had the opportunity, as guest lecturer at some supper, to pick up one or two pieces of pastry, carry them home in a lunch sack, and drop them with a pleased smile into his little girl's mouth. He pasted together a shimmering paper dragon for his little boy and let it hang from the roof of the house during the boys' festival. Then crossing his legs he would let himself down on the "tatami" to play, Kayano on his one side, and Makoto on the other. Midori, on the sofa, would lay her silk painting aside and read Poro's latest medical treatise, without understanding a word.

"Papa! Papa!" Makoto would start begging. "Go on with the last story you were telling! Did Father Battista reach the martyrs' hill in our city or did he break on the way? Did his little Mass server, Louis, bleed to death with his ears chopped off? Did brave little Thomas' mother have a chance to say good-bye to her darling at the bamboo fence?"

44

Father Nagai retold the story of the great martyrs of Nagasaki to his children like a pastor or a missionary. And when the great peace of Sunday would steal in upon the family, the father with his big son at his arm and mother with her little girl on her back would follow the invitation of the bells to the cathedral.

In 1937, when the conflict with China broke out, Dr. Nagai was called to service as the chief doctor of the Fifth Medical Corps, and it was not until March, 1940, that he was able to return to his family on their peaceful island.

"Mrs. Sadoko, Mrs. Tagawa, Mrs. Fukabori! Won't you be my guests today?" Often in those three lonely years Mrs. Nagai called through the thin paper walls to her neighbors and invited them in to sample her cooking. As a former home economics instructress, she discovered a new dish during the hard days of the war, made of pine needles and maple leaves.

The week had too few days for her, and the day too few hours, especially now that she had been elected president of the big women's society of Urakami. Mrs. Nagai took care of the public kitchen during air raids; she organized the emergency campaign, and gave courses at the nearby factory in flower decorating, in needlework, and in tea party ceremonies. She passed many a sleepless night at her singing sewing machine. From time to time she would turn up the lamp and relax momentarily while she read a verse on a Haiku-ribbon.

> Look! The fluttering leaf!
> On the mound of that grave
> It has stopped to rest.
>
> —Ransetsu.

> A hasty seeking of shelter
> Before a rainstorm—
> Believe me, life is nothing more.
>
> —Sogi.

And then her thoughts would turn to Poro on the battlefield.

IV

Friend and Murderer Alike

From 1941 onward Dr. Nagai was always on his way with a stack of X-ray photos from the photography room to the therapy room, from the laboratory to the X-ray room. Now and then he would change his direction, but never the tempo, hurrying from the X-ray room to the photo room, from the laboratory to therapy. He was ever the same: busy as a bee, the nervous, active Japanese in a constant state of electrification, moving with short, quick motions, vibrating in every muscle of his face. He never had time to warm a seat or to wait for the elevator. Usually he took the stairs two at a time. Out of pure zeal for his work he would often forget to shield himself sufficiently from the rays at his machine. He never had time.

How could it possibly be otherwise? After all, the war between Japan and the Allies had snatched away all of his colleagues in the radiological institute. Some of his assistants were called away from their fluorescent screens to go to Formosa; other technicians left the laboratory for the Philippines. Only the inexperienced girls stayed behind. Dr. Nagai was at once the chief, assistant, technician, researcher, professor of the X-ray department, and a doctor with many other duties besides. If he had cared to, he could have signed his letters with a different title every day for a week!

In the first year of the war the national defense program was still piling up great depots of supplies. With heroism and the "harikari" spirit of the Samurai, Japan would be able to last through ten long years of war! But the people were hungry, and the doctors were running out of medicine and film.

The research expert of Nagasaki was inventive, however. He merely brought his indirect radiography to a stop and satisfied himself with directly irradiating his patients. Then the spreading rays, like a countless horde of little devils, chased after the exposed and defenseless operator, who could not shake them off.

If only the endless procession of the sick could have slowed down! In normal times, the first patient would usually knock early in the morning, the second would come limping up around the afternoon tea, and the third toward evening. But now, at the beginning of the consultation hour, the Sister would announce: "Twenty are waiting, and thirty have reported already." Coughing TB patients, patients with wasted bones from vitamin deficiencies, shirkers and deserters from the army, wounded with splintered limbs from the air raids. There were besides the hundred professional visits that Dr. Nagai made each day with his assistant Shi, and the lectures on radiology he had to give.

"Am I not perhaps committing suicide? A slow 'harikari'?" Dr. Nagai asked himself. Without an answer he turned to his apparatus, an ironical smile on his lips. The sick-nurse rang: "New patients, Doctor."

The internees and the nurses looked and pointed at him with alarm. The professor, as he worked with his X-ray machine, dangled his chronically inflamed hands over his patients, trying to make himself forget the aching pain of the radiation disease he was contracting. And it was during these days that he scratched in his diary: "It is the duty of a doctor to suffer with his patients and to count himself glad. To worry about their troubles, to ease their pains as if they were his own. He has to feel their pain with them, does he not?"

On a hot June day in 1945, after irradiating his fiftieth patient, Dr. Nagai broke down before the fluorescent screen. The nurse on duty took him by the hand past the frightened medical students to his private room on the third floor. A small hill of notes and scraps, a whole mountain of graphic sketches, and an irregular mountain chain of X-ray photos were piled on his work table. If only his work were ended!

At his writing desk, weak and trembling, he dipped his brush into the ink and finished his diary, as if it were his will at the approach of death. "Still, in the last analysis, it is not the medicine that helps the sick, but the kindness of God. If that is once understood, then a doctor's diagnosis turns into a prayer."

It had become quite still. There was not a sound to disturb him. The top of a camphor tree outside the window filtered the sunlight softly into the room. Dr. Nagai's tired eyes fell on the great white statue of the Blessed Virgin above his writing table. He took his rosary from his pocket and recommended all the patients he had ever treated to her, the comforter of the afflicted.

Sister Superior brought him some weak tea, placed a bouquet of lilies beside the statue, and left without a sound. He leaned back in his swivel chair, and in the space of a minute he lived through his toilsome rise to success, saw his modern X-ray institute with its eight examination rooms before him, and asked himself, "Where did I get the strength for that?"—then quickly he gave the answer: "From the Catholic Faith."

With a little nod he dozed off. Two of his girl laboratory assistants woke him up with a large stack of X-ray photos. They whispered in front of his door. "Something is not quite right with the Professor! If only he isn't really sick!"

"Why, what's wrong with our good man the chief? Sleeping in broad daylight?" this was the third time the two gay young medical students had asked themselves that question in Sister Superior's room. They were overjoyed at the thought of a day without classes. Then the door opened. Dr. Nagai was standing on the threshold, chatting and laughing, and beaming all over at how well things were turning out. He was discoursing on the joys of science and in conclusion he told them with a sly look, "Only those can taste this joy who really and truly experiment. You can't just work with your head. Unless you study with your whole self, there is no result. . . ."

"Doctor! In these last months you always seem to fall asleep as soon as you sit down, even for a little bit. And at the word 'patient' you jump right up again!" Sister Superior voiced her worries before the little group.

"Yes, yes indeed. For a half year now I've been most uncommonly sleepy."

"You must certainly be seriously ill."

"Really?"

"You ought to have a thorough examination."

"Now, that's a good idea." And with that Dr. Nagai made his way painfully to the X-ray room and ordered Urakawa, who was just beginning to clean the instrument board, "Please prepare everything for an irradiation. Here is the patient and the doctor as well."

"Oho! Two birds with one stone," Urakawa

wanted to say in jest; but he kept his silence, feeling that this was a serious case.

Dr. Nagai accustomed his eyes to the dark and threw himself down on the old chair. Tens of thousands had awaited their diagnosis here, coughing, spitting, groaning. Now, suddenly, the anxiety of these ten thousand stormed up in the X-ray doctor and would not let him free. Now he was standing on the podium, just as ten thousand had stood there before him, shivering and shaking, not because of the cold, but for the future. This time he was afraid for himself, for his wife, and for his children.

He drew the fluorescent screen into place before his body and commanded briskly, "Shoot!" He closed his eyes again.

"How unfeelingly, how coldly, like an iceberg, have I not always handled my patients!" The thought shot through his head. Then he leaned forward and looked at the screen.

"Ah," he sighed. But as doctor he caught hold of himself. Coolly and dispassionately he examined a most interesting disease. The whole left side of his body was filled with big black spots from a disordered spleen. The liver was swollen. The heart in its cavity below the breast was slightly displaced.

"Leukemia, atomic disease!" Dr. Nagai gave his expert analysis to the frightened patient Nagai.

He called Dr. Shi. With his finger he circled the phenomena of the disease on the screen and explained it to his student: "This is a very special case. You will want to examine it more closely."

Without suspecting anything, his assistant, Inoue, announced: "Professor, the fourth class is ready for the lecture." Heroically Dr. Nagai answered from the podium, "Thank you; I'll come at once."

After the lecture Dr. Nagai sank into a chair in the X-ray room and entered his discovery on the card index by himself. "Chronic leukemia of the marrow. White corpuscles, instead of 7000—100,000. Red corpuscles, instead of five million—three million. Duration of life, three years. Disease incurable—with painful death."

The exhausted man looked at the X-ray machine and spoke to himself. "You were my friend and my murderer at the same time. You made me a research technician, and took my life in return. But you have healed tens of thousands, and crippled only one. That makes the difference. Besides, you have grown old. Your varnish is peeling off. And you are covered over back and forth with insulating tape. Who managed to bring you so far? I did—I, Dr. Nagai. Your life-time is running out, too."

A messenger came to the X-ray doctor on this day in June, telling him that the rector of the university was calling for him. In his private office the rector stared at him as if he were frozen in his armchair. Quite embarrassed, he slid the register of the university students from the right side of his desk to the left. He could find no fitting word to say and laid the register on the right side again. Finally he stammered: "I have received word of your condition. The pain in my heart is too great. Forgive me, but I have to say it. If you were to leave us, you would put me in a most embarrassing situation. The functioning of the whole department depends on you. And without our X-ray department we could no longer prepare a thorough diagnosis. You see that, if you leave, we will all be hard pressed."

Red with shame at having made this plea, the rector once more reached for the register. With a slight bow Dr. Nagai explained his willingness to make this new and final surrender of his life to his fellow men, and he forgave the rector for all his earlier witticisms about radiology.

* * *

But what would he tell his wife that evening? He who had always been waiting for the hour in which he could whisper in Midori's ear, "Just think, I have been promoted to form-master! Just think, a promotion at the hospital! Dearest! Now you no longer have to work part-time in the factory!"

Instead of a form-master, Midori would now have a cripple for a husband—and after she had

57

struggled through eleven years as a professor's wife.

"Yes, what that must mean, to have me as a husband," the thought shot through his hammering head on the way home. Resting on his bamboo cane, he caught his breath a moment. "Whenever I got home, I always loved my X-ray machine more than my wife. I kept working at my research on my desk. I asked for a cup of tea when I must have known that there was no fire left in the kitchen, and then left it untouched beside my manuscripts. Then I would be harsh with the children when they made noise, and a few minutes later forget what I had said or done. And didn't I hurry every night, when I did go home at all, to take my pad from beneath my pillow and scribble down some formula?"

At his house, Dr. Nagai stopped tor a moment before the garden wall and thought once more. "Midori! If I hadn't had you, how often would I not have gone to work without my tie? And you forgave me so readily that time I passed you on the street, sunken in thought like a sleepwalker, and did not know you. And will you forgive me now? Now that I have saved others through my love for research, and have passed a hard and bitter judgment on you and the children?"

That evening Midori was lying on the "tatami" beside Poro, with her four-year-old daughter on her arm. Gently stirred by the cool breeze from the sea, the woven straw motto shone from the wall:

> You say that life is short:
> I thought that a dream was long.

Kayano was playing with her little doll. Outside it grew very still and almost dark. The peace of evening! Poro moved his pillow closer to Midori and stammered into her ear, "Gomen nasai— forgive me!" And he told her about his incurable disease.

Midori grasped the little girl tighter in her arms and listened without a motion. Then she gave Kayano to her father, who was finishing his story.

"Our little son, Makoto, will carry on the X-ray research where I left off."

Now Midori was standing; she went over to the house altar in silence, lighted the candles, and sank to the floor without a word, her eyes upon the crucifix, praying.

With a helpless look, Poro followed her. Midori's shoulders were trembling in the flickering candlelight. It seemed that Poro's wife had never been so great, so noble. He leaned his head on that of his little daughter, helpless, feeling guilty and repentant.

Poro murmured softly, "I have always known that, just as Christ said, every suffering must be accepted and borne as a cross. But this heroic attitude, this attitude that corresponds so well with the teaching of Jesus, will I manage to keep it until my last breath? Lord, lead me not into temptation. Be merciful to me; don't give me more than I can bear with my little strength."

Midori stood once more, prepared now to take

a new cross upon her shoulders—prepared even to carry her husband home from the university if she had to. She took her place beside Poro and said, "Life or death, everything for the greater honor and glory of God."

V

The Three Angels of the Apocalypse

"Is our little pig fat enough yet?" Bill asked jokingly.

"Not yet," Jim took him up quietly. "No, not yet. But by this time Tuesday we'll have a fatter one."

A pair of men with anxious, careworn faces were looking after the pig. They had penned it in a windowless room, heavily guarded.

Now and then a groaning thunder could be heard in the distance. "Attention! Attention!" announced an excited voice on the shortwave sender ten feet from the quiet group of workers. "President Truman has just given out the secret. The uncanny weapon that was used on August 6 over Hiroshima, called an 'atom bomb' . . ."

The men were electrified; they took a long step backwards and stared at each other as if they were frozen to the spot. Their looks seemed to say, "So here we are on the Island of Tinian in the Marianas, and all of a sudden the spot becomes the center of world attention!" They let out a sigh of relief, and Henry blurted out, "Let's forget about this 'little pig' business and the secret language, and start putting our atom bomb together!"

Beneath the dark and threatening sky they lifted the meteor that had grown up in their hands into the wide bomb bay of a B-29, together with its complicated mechanism weighing several tons. One or two flashes of lightning blazed and ripped through the black night sky.

General Farrell appeared at midnight in their barn-like barracks with an unusual order to give.

The crews of the three superforts jumped to their feet from their rough-hewn wooden benches. General Farrell stepped onto a high podium and spoke to them in short, commanding sentences: "The industrial center on Kyushu is your goal. Over the island of Yakoshima at 0910 wait for the weather report and group. Throw your load directly on the target only if you have full visibility—otherwise turn around. Subs and rescue ships are stationed at all points in case of a forced landing. In case of capture, the bearer of this document is promoted to superior. In case of fog over Z, wait 45 minutes. Then turn for Nagasaki." General Farrell saluted and left the room.

The kindly Field Chaplain came into the room as the general left, folded his hands one over the other, bowed his head, and lifted his thin, beseeching voice. "Almighty God, Father of Grace, we pray you, let your Grace come down upon the men who will fly in this night. Guard and protect those of us who will venture forth into the darkness of your heaven. Lead them on your wings. Guard their bodies and their souls and bring them back to us. Give us all courage and strength for the hours that lie before us, and reward us according to the hardships they will bring. But above all, my Father, give Your world peace. Let us go our way trusting in You and secure in the knowledge that You are near to us now and for all eternity. Amen."

*   *   *

The weather observers had already taken off by dawn. Then the orange-colored, four-bladed propellers of the three B-29's began to turn with a whirring noise. Eighteen men were wrapped in their flak suits and life-jackets, wedged in between arsenals of apparatus, cables, and cameras. Their parachutes, rubber boat, and oxygen masks were close at hand. At 0350 the three machines took off into the starless, storming morning of August 9.

Major Sweeny flew the lead plane, Great Artist, to the northwest, toward Japan. Captain Ashworth was his co-pilot. Bombardier Kermit from Texas was just celebrating his twenty-seventh birthday. With one clutch at his instruments he would let loose the atom bomb that fated morning and plot the fall of a destructive power that was equal to 4000 blockbusters.

Two other B-29's followed closely behind, mounted with special, highly sensitive instruments to record the destruction of a city by camera. William Laurence was flying as journalist and reporter in the first observation plane. He was making a sketch of the last battle report of the Second World War. With the power of 8000 winged horses the three machines sped through the air.

A storm broke out at 17000 feet. The planes veered downward into bottomless gorges of cloud, then panted their way back up with a mighty roar and dropped down again into the thick darkness of hidden air pockets. The whirring propellers had been transformed into burning disks. They painted the ridges of the clouds a ghostly violet. Now blue flames sprang out of the cabin of the lead plane, shooting from the window panes and dancing along the wings.

Atomic rays? The beginning of the explosion? No, St. Elmo's Fire, a load of static electricity.

Like shining speedboats, the three B-29's drove along the seething waves of the cumulus clouds. From the start all the crews had their earphones on; now they also put on their oxygen masks. The temperature outside the plane was 33 below zero. The cabin was heated to a comfortable warmth. But a frosty silence and a loneliness crept in among the crews. So they swung along through the dark night of the universe, these new conquerors of the world, each with his own thoughts. Distorted images rose up in their minds. Charred skeletons snatched after them. Whitened skulls gaped at them out of the black cavities that were once their eyes. Whimpering orphan children lifted their tiny fists against them.

Shortly after 0500 pale streaks of light appeared, the first signs of dawn. "It's good to see day again," remarked Sergeant Ralph D. Curry, alongside William Laurence in the first escort plane. "I get scared when I'm penned up all night in a cabin like this. Do you suppose this atom bomb will end the war?"

"It's very probable that this will do it; and if it doesn't, then surely the next one will, or the one after that. Their power is so great that no nation can resist them for very long."

At 0550 it was day. The morning flooded down upon the three bombers like a waterfall of light and sun. The immeasurable ocean in the depths below and the vast heavens above them melted into one great sphere. From their lookout tower, 17000 feet above the sea, they had an unobstructed view for hundreds of miles. Now and then a mountain of clouds humped up before them, and with a loud groan the motors bored a tunnel through it. Behind these steaming clouds a city was waking up to its last day of sunlight. The weather had not yet decided whether it was to be Z or Nagasaki, however. It was 0900. The pilots adjusted a few dials. They all climbed into their parachutes.

The machines climbed to the proper altitude to

release the bomb. They were now over Japanese waters, circling over the Island of Yakoshima, southwest of Kyushu, in order to regroup. "Sunny sighting over Z and Nagasaki," Major Ralph D. Curry translated the coded message from the weather observers. The minutes of a long quarter hour ticked slowly by. The second escort plane was still missing. Another quarter hour and it still was not there. After 45 minutes Major Sweeny ordered the last loop.

The Great Artist, followed by the first observation plane, swung over Z. Over Kagoshima? Sasebo? Omuda? No one knows. The radar screen showed the industrial center of Z. It was now lying under a fog. In the costly three quarters of an hour the Japanese winds had blown it in. Fifteen flak bursts spurted up, but fell too low. Eight more followed, too wide to the left. The pilots banked out of the fire zone—the observers spied a rift in the fog—the bombardier reached toward the release lever—then 21 Japanese interceptors whistled down through the cloudy sky.

"Old friend, that was the last story you will write," the thought jumped through William Laurence's head. Death was clutching at him and the whole crew. But the fighters withdrew; they took the squadron of two for weather planes. Stubbornly the Great Artist circled over Z once again. The peep-hole had to open. The bomb had to fall here. But the mist had formed a conspiracy against the almighty weapon.

A quick turn of the wheel threw the lead plane toward Nagasaki, signaling to the observation plane to follow. But even this smiling city was hiding coyly behind a veil of cloud. The radar-scope trained on the munitions factory and the ship works. Now the seconds became hours, and the minutes eternities. The fuel supply had sunk to a minimum. In the next few seconds the veil of fog would have to lift. The bomb would have to drop.

The first circle was completed—no rift was visible. Major Sweeny and Captain Ashworth took counsel. "What should we do—turn back—hold on till the last drop of gas—try a forced drop—jump and sacrifice ourselves—?" In the last minutes the fog split—for a few short moments Nagasaki lay open below them—the streaming noon light pouring over her.

The prearranged signal sounded on the radio set. Everyone put on his heavy glasses. The clocks showed high noon. The last seconds of Nagasaki's life ticked away . . . ten—twenty—thirty—fifty—fifty-five—fifty-eight—fifty-nine. . . .

"There it goes!" shouted someone in the observation plane.

A dark object fell from the womb of the Great Artist. It was 1201, Thursday, August 9, 1945.

"Forced landing, without circling!" Major Sweeny radioed on the way to the base at Okinawa. But the emergency signal refused to go off. "Wounded aboard!" he announced at the last minute. The fuel tanks were almost dry. Three hours and seventeen minutes had slipped away over the Japanese island. Several signals in B-29

71

jargon followed each other in rapid succession. . . .

On Okinawa comfortable ambulances rolled out on to the field. Doctors and chaplains rushed up to give their aid. In the sun of the early afternoon two bombers hovered over the crystal surface of the ocean around the island. The motors knocked and beat irregularly. Halfway down the runway two of them went out for lack of fuel. The crews escaped death by a few seconds.

Someone rushed up to the planes with the excited announcement, "Russia has just entered the war."

VI

Inferno Over Nagasaki

The sun playfully peeped down on Nagasaki from behind Mount Kompira that Thursday morning of August 9, 1945. Slowly it climbed higher, stopping dead still in triumph for a few minutes on the lowest peak, to smile for the last time on all the splendor below it, roguish and serene. Then its rays tumbled down in merry confusion upon the hills of the city, enchanting and gilding everything: the roofs of the houses, the dew on the potato leaves, the broad Urakami River, and the narrow straits nearby. Happy and content, it sparkled down on the gray yellow columns of smoke that wound up from the munitions factory, and on the procession of white-clad pilgrims who were going toward the cathedral.

Mrs. Nagai was up in her little garden early in the morning, dragging the heavy fertilizer box back and forth. The rosy azaleas she tended were sparkling beautifully this year in the sun of Kyushu, and the chrysanthemums were already in bud. What an enchanting spectacle they would make around the doctor's house in the fall! The happy Manju festival, on the feast of the Assumption, was only one week away, and then Midori would bake the traditional Manju cakes and let the fragrance of the sweet jelly fill the house. She shook out a basketful of soy beans to dry in the garden, and went back to see the neighbors.

"And how is Dr. Nagai this morning?" Taka Urata was wondering. With her daughters and two neighbors she was squatting on the pillows in the "engawa" of the doctor's house.

"Last night he slept at the University," Midori answered, and, embarrassedly, she wiped a silvery spider web from the bulgy paper lantern at the entrance of the "engawa." "I think I'll get some lunch ready for him now and bring it over to him. I wish I had some ham in the house. . . ."

"Well, how is he?" Urata repeated, and pulled her kimono over her feet. "Does it look as if he'll get better?"

"No; when someone is sick and works as much as he does," sighed Midori, and took a step or two away. . . . " No, he isn't well. I'm terribly worried. Please, won't you all say a special prayer for him? Fine."

The conversation was brought to an abrupt close by the screaming of the sirens. The women bowed a goodbye to each other and took their leave. "Do you want to come to the mill with me, Cousin Midori?" Kikone begged through the narrow opening in the paper door.

"No, Kikone, not now; I have to bring my husband his lunch first. Then I'm going to Koba to see after the children who were evacuated."

A few minutes later the flash of the atom surprised Midori at her kitchen hearth, engaged in the last selfless service of a faithful wife. She had only a few seconds to take her rosary into her hand. . . .

* * *

"Planes over Kyushu!" screamed the loud-speaker —the alarm went through all the corridors—it spread through the reception rooms and the laboratories—all the sickrooms heard it—the whole university clinic was electrified. Doctors and professors, students and nurses hurried through the passages with their masks and first aid provisions at their sides, dragging patients on stretchers into the shelter room. They went after the water buckets, and placed the little pickaxes and small shovels within reach.

Dr. Nagai, the head and director of air raid defense, hurried into the west wing, his forehead wrinkled with care. Conscientiously he opened the latch on each door and put his head into every room.

"We live and die as fate has determined for us.

Let us live and die so that no one shall despise us," an air raid warden, beaded with sweat, said to him.

"No more enemy planes over the island," the loud-speaker announced. The lectures and consultations resumed. Dr. Nagai stood in his white doctor's apron in the laboratory again, above the patients' consultation room on the first floor of the concrete west wing, putting X-ray films in order in his immense card index. He had already been summoned by death. With his hollow cheeks and his jutting cheek bones he was a walking skeleton. He had been busy the night before on air raid patrol, and had managed only a few short hours of sleep sitting on a bench in the lecture hall, his head on his crossed arms. Today his work was not flitting as easily as usual through his quick fingers, and his tired head was not on the job. Every photograph of some poor patient seemed to be telling him, "That is the way you too will soon look, sunken to a skeleton, choked by a deadly asthma, always spitting blood."

Coughing now and then, the professor wiped the

perspiration from his bony forehead with the narrow back of his hand, sorting photo after photo into the file. Now and then, completely lost in thought, he would lift his eyes to a picture of this or that reproachful patient, and murmur with quiet resignation, "But Midori will watch at my bed; Midori will cool my feverish lips, she will say the prayers for the dying with me, press the crucifix to my dying forehead; in her arms I will draw my last breath. Then, with the courage of her selfless soul she will close my eyes and follow my body to the grave. Midori! You will transfigure my dying moments!"

Sunk in thought, Dr. Nagai suddenly saw his wife before him, just as he had left her yesterday. Once again he had forgotten the lunch that Midori had prepared for him almost reverently in a flower-covered little bag. Once again he had turned back. He had found her on the "engawa," on the pillows all rumpled together. That was goodbye, the last time he saw her.

* * *

A blinding flash of lightning split the firmament in two and fell in blue and purple down over Urakami. A seething storm swept over the roofs of the city, five to ten times stronger than a hurricane. An icy wind plunged after it with a force of more than 600 miles per hour. A fiery furnace, of almost 6000 degrees, as hot as the surface of the sun, flared up. Ashes and charred bits of paper whirled through the air. The dark of late evening broke over the city at high noon. The atom bomb had exploded fifteen hundred feet over the suburban and industrial section of Urakami, and broke downward like a foretaste of judgment day.

Forty-five seconds slipped by before the first wave of the explosion was heard, followed by four other earth-shaking bursts. Then the earth spit out a giant ball of fire which grew into a purple column 10,000 feet in the air in the fraction of a second. The bottom turned brown-black and measured over three miles. The shaft of the column was yellow gold; its point was a blinding white spread out over a good half mile. Now a giant mushroom burst out of the top and lengthened the shaft to 45,000 feet. From this height a satanic fireworks hissed down upon the city of Nagasaki with a thousand sparks. It seethed and boiled with all the colors of the rainbow. Its beams reached out 200 miles, painting the river valley of the Urakami and the surrounding hills now red and blue, now green and brown.

Those of the terrified inhabitants who were still alive had ducked behind a tree trunk, or thrown themselves flat on the ground. They dug their fingers into the dust or clutched at the bark of the tree, and tried to find a name for the apocalyptic horror: "Monster clouds, volcanic springs," they stammered, "a fire tree!"

In a circle of two miles the peaceful little houses, with their cultivated fruit and flower gardens, had been simply blown away, and in the ruins one fire after another broke out. In a few minutes a whole section of the city was one single sea of flames. With the foaming column of fire and

80

smoke and gas the whole valley of the Urakami River had been changed into a seething hell.

Nature was desecrated and thrown off her course. The sun above Kyushu was hidden behind soot and cinders. The animals died. The chirp of the crickets and the trilling of canaries ceased. The camellia and the cherry trees had only their splintered trunks to stretch into the air, like angry fists. In the gardens the cabbages and gourds were cut away, and the polished stone paths were melted into dirty green glass: it cooled much too quickly and was filled with cracks and splinters.

A rain of fat oil drops ate through the mighty leaves of the taro trees. Radios and electric currents were broken off. In a few crooked houses the tiny lights from candle holders shone strangely through the uncanny noonday darkness.

Where were the people? The smiling inhabitants of this tropical city, with their fans in their hands and the cherry blossoms in their hair? They had become like primitives and cave men. "Mitsuyoshi! Mitsuyoshi? My husband?" cried Mrs. Kome and pressed Machiko, her youngest son, close to her breast. With singed hair and torn kimono she staggered from one little fire-free patch to another. She did not notice how Machiko, killed by the rays, suddenly dropped his little head to the side. She only held him tighter in her arms and stumbled over a stiff body in the playground of the school. "Mitsuyoshi!" she gasped, and sank down in a heap on top of her badly burned husband with her dead child, laughing the hollow, meaningless laugh of an hysterical person.

"Give us water. We're dying of thirst. Cover us. We're freezing. Where is Mama? Get our Mama. Isn't Dr. Nagai coming, Dr. Nagai!" A chorus of suffering arose from a black air raid shelter. Crying children clawed at the side of their teachers. Women in labor were lying stretched out on the bare earth. Trembling old men crowded together into a corner. Everybody cried for a few drops of water; and hardly had they gulped it down when they vomited it back up. . . .

The quiet August night cast a soft veil over the half sunken city. The darkness covered the holes and rents in the earth, the pain and longing of the survivors. In the houses that had been spared along the terraces by the hill an occasional little light still fluttered. Kneeling on the "tatamis," the Catholics began saying their rosaries for their 8,500 dead fellow Christians. Nor did they forget the 25,000 dead of all creeds and the more than 100,000 wounded.

VII

The Good Samaritan among the Ruins

Part of the flaming destruction dropped down from the noonday heavens upon the university clinic. The windows burst inwards. An oven-like blast of wind howled through the rooms and halls, took the professor of radiology off his feet, and lifted him into the air. A rain of splinters rattled down upon him. . . .

Now Dr. Nagai was buried alive under the ruins of beds and chairs and chests. "Midori! My last hour has come! Do not forget to say the prayers with me," he groaned. Bits of clothing, pieces of metal, and X-ray photos flew around the room in a wild dance, and outside the ear-splitting thunder of the explosion accompanied the raining ashes. The night of the Apocalypse had begun, and suddenly, out of the dark, Midori, with the unobstructed flight of a soul redeemed, stood for a moment before the dust-gray countenance of her Poro to say goodbye. He had just called for her; but now he had other work to do.

"How many patients are there? Where shall I bring them? Into the classroom? But first I shall have to get free myself!" He twisted his shoulders, drew up his knees. The debris ground and scratched him; the fragments stuck like thorns. Then he rubbed his eyelids. They were wet with blood. He could see nothing. His right temple was badly cut. "Blinded? Robbed of the light of my eyes?" he asked himself in fright and moaned for help. "Tasukete kure!—Tasukete kure!" "Help, please! Help!"

A few yards away in the X-ray room the laboratory assistant, Hashimoto, stared through the broken window out into a sea of flames. "An absolute inferno," she gasped.

"Tasukete kure!" she heard the echo. "Tasukete kure!"

Didn't Dr. Nagai always give orders like that, so quickly and firmly? "Tasukete kure!" Really it must be he. Hashimoto climbed over the dented pieces of metal from the X-ray machine, jumped across the electric wires, stumbled over a crushed patient who was flooded with red light in the reflection of the flames. "Eternal rest give unto him, O Lord," she called after the dead man, and felt her way forward.

"Is this the end of the world? Why, the sun must have fallen! It can't be only a bomb." Five assistants and Sisters were crouching behind an immense table that they had turned over for shelter with their last ounce of strength.

Then Hashimoto burst in, panting heavily, and fell to her knees before them. "Dr. Nagai! Just think; Dr. Nagai is buried alive!"

"My God," was the answer, "and he's so big. How shall we ever get him out?"

Over a doorpost which lay across their path they crawled to the shattered window, climbed down the lightning conductor, rounded up a ladder, and climbed back into the laboratory of the X-ray chief. With a few splintered boards that once belonged to a chair or a desk they shoveled the buried doctor out of his grave.

Then they congratulated him on his escape, with ice cold hands, without a word. The half-darkened photo room had been torn into a labyrinth of gaping holes and cracks, and an abyss of silence and wonder fell over the chief and his assistants. His sight marred by blood, Dr. Nagai gazed down on a line of anxious eyes. Then he stared dumbly in the distance, and whispered, ". . . and the others? Where are they?—Look for them; save them, please!"

"Umezu, Inoue, Yamashita!" Dr. Shi called through the darkness and the heavy rain of ashes. The Sisters shoved a shattered beam aside and picked up half a door. Then a weak voice moaned from the corner. A whole chorus joined it. A

87

"Miserere" of suffering rose up from many throats. "Save us, Doctor. Medicine, please! Mama, put a bandage on my cut! I'm bleeding to death!"

Half-naked figures rose out of the dark gray of the blackness following the explosion, which turned a livid red from time to time in the light of the distant fountains of flame. They were gray with the surrounding dust but were still on their way to see the doctor. Now they clutched at his frayed coat and begged for help.

Those who could no longer do that, pointed with silent gestures to the blood trickling from their wounds. Like a good Samaritan, Dr. Nagai stood among them. His own right hand pressed against his open temple, he bound together the sections of skin that were hanging loose, the swollen lips, the open blisters.

"That's all the gauze we have," complained the tired voice of the laboratory assistant, "and there isn't a single instrument to be found. Besides that, there are a good thirty, probably at least fifty, patients lying in the corridor."

"Then we'll rip up our shirts," answered the determined X-ray doctor. The blood from his own wound dropped in a sharp arch on to the shoulder of his nurse and sprinkled bright red spots along the gray wall. "We can't get anywhere in this whirlwind of dust," commanded Dr. Nagai. With a piece of bandage in his hand he ordered, "Call all the air raid warden groups together. Get the emergency drugs. Bring out the reserve supplies. Carry the patients to the main entrance. Keep calm and be brave."

"But, professor, your own wounds," admonished an assistant and firmly made his chief lean over a creaking card-index cabinet. Then he quickly wrapped an emergency bandage around his temples. Dr. Shi brought him the shoe he had lost. His dented air raid helmet in his left hand and his dirty overcoat in his right, Dr. Nagai hurried conscientiously over the twisted potted palms through the dusky corridor. An hysterical woman stood in their path, dancing, her hair fluttering. A few of the students had stopped in groups of two and three and stared in silence after their professor.

Arriving at the main gate, Dr. Nagai saw a procession of misery tottering toward him. Anxious mothers were bringing their maimed children to the hospital. Two trembling old men, their arms about each other's neck, came toward him. Three children pulled their dead father before his feet. At that moment the flames hissed with a fearful crackling in the west wing, and a strong blast of wind brought the whimpering death cries from the city to Dr. Nagai's ears.

"Leave all your instruments! Evacuate the patients from all the rooms! First into the coal cellar, then on to the nearby hill!" the head doctor cried into the panic from below the front gate. The blood-soaked bandage around his head was now like a flaming red turban. His twenty helpers rushed with him through the rooms, protecting themselves against the flames and smoke with their handkerchiefs in front of their mouths and noses. A patient himself, bowed under the weight of two sick men, Dr. Nagai climbed through the creaking ruins of the overthrown walls, and up the steep hill. Drops of blood from the wounds on his temples rolled to the ground and splashed in front of him on the shattered tiles of the road.

Some of the patients were moved to a potato field on a low hill. A thick rain began to fall. Like drops of heavy oil it ate its way into the rags and blankets of the sick. Dr. Nagai hurried from bed to bed, bent over each individual patient, and smiled a cheerful "Sasaki gambare" to him. Then he was off to the next one, whispering a consoling "Be brave" into his ear. From the arms of a dying mother he took her two-month-old child and fondled it. . . . Then someone cried out suddenly, "The photograph room is burning!"

"That is the end of everything," Dr. Nagai could not help saying. He sat down with the little child on the ground, in the middle of the field, and cried like a child himself, covering his face with both hands, as if he were confronted with a horror that no one could wish to look upon. The nurses bent over him, but could not hold back any longer and sobbed with him. The clinic was one mass of flames. Only ten professors, four-fifths of the students, and fifty of the wardens were saved.

Toward evening an assistant spread a white cloth over the ground. Dr. Nagai drew a red circle over the center with his bloodsoaked bandage, fastened it to a bamboo stick, and planted it in the field. High from the hilltop, over the smouldering university and the dying city, the flag of Japan with its rising sun waved in the evening breeze.

Umezu, one of the assistants, was lying unconscious among the singed ferns. Dr. Nagai covered him with his own coat. That was his last act of service. He dropped to the ground beside Umezu, dead tired. Confusedly he crumpled a lump of earth between his fingers and murmured to himself, "Now I know. She is dead. I know it. Midori is dead. Otherwise she would have come right over the crackling coals, leaning on a bamboo cane, with a dish full of rice and fish. Yes, you would have felt your way to me with your hands, half a mile; you would have crawled to me on your knees. Midori; I know it." With that he rolled over on one side and lost consciousness.

"Some more thread. A clamp. Gauze!" ordered Dr. Shi, who finally could set to work on his professor's head wound. Then Dr. Nagai came to and tottered with his colleagues and the faithful Sisters to a little shelter of straw and reeds for the rest of the night. An uneasy quiet lay over the hill of Nagasaki. The oppressive silence of the night was interrupted only by the light crackling of a low fire, warming tea for the sick men. The patients had all fallen asleep, or else passed on to the deeper slumber of death. Not a fly was buzzing. They had all been burned to death. The cloud from the explosion had lifted and was still shining down upon them, dark red in the distance. It was almost midnight.

Suddenly from the opposite hill two swords of fire hissed up into the night sky. The cathedral was smouldering and painted a final background for the tragedy. This same night, in the palace at Tokyo, the Emperor was pacing restlessly back and forth. Then, at a late hour, he called his generals and made known to them his decision— he would capitulate, in order not to have another bomb. The high officers paced about in their shining uniforms. With loud sobs and tears in their eyes they entreated the Emperor.

*   *   *

On the following day, August 10, the sun rose over Mount Kompira on a city that had half disappeared. Its rays glided over the shattered tiles in the blockaded streets, streaking the splintered trees that lay about like kindling wood. Dr. Nagai climbed down the hill and walked with Dr. Shi through his burned-out radiological institute. His first stop was at the debris-strewn grave of his missing colleagues. His companion was reading a leaflet dropped from the airplane, charred along the edges. Without a word he handed it to him. Dr. Nagai read:

"To the Japanese people! America has succeeded in inventing a weapon . . . its power is equal to the bomb capacity of 2000 B-29's. . . . We have used this weapon against Japan. . . . We beg you to make every possible request to your Emperor that he cease hostilities. The President of the United States has already delivered his proviso, in 13 points, for an honorable submission. For a new, peaceful, better Japan. Otherwise we shall not hesitate to use this bomb again. . . ."

Suddenly Dr. Nagai reached for the bamboo pole, which was sticking up from the ground and cracking with the strain. His eyes were filled with tears as he lifted it high in the air. He wanted to shout a mighty threat, but he could not make a sound. Choked with emotion, his throat was held shut as with an iron band. Gasping and coughing, he finally managed to stammer, "An atomic bomb, then. Japan is—conquered. Science—will

95

celebrate a great triumph—but our native island —has had a heavy blow."

The joy of the physicist and radium researcher was fighting with the deep pain of the patriot. The bamboo stick in his right hand and the leaflet in his left, the professor stumbled with his bandaged head slowly and wearily up the hill to see his patients.

* * *

The next day, August 11, all the patients were carried into the military hospital. Dr. Nagai received permission from the director of the hospital to go home. If he only could! If he could only walk once more past the well and through the garden gate with his theme papers in his hand. If only he could pick a red camellia blossom behind the house and surprise Midori and the children! No, he could no longer go home—to a pile of ashes.

With the matted blood-red bandage around his head, he stood calmly before the ruins of his little house. He was speechless and lost, like an exile in the most solitary desert, like a prisoner in the blackest cell. A disconnected, evil smelling shaft of smoke rose up between the broken porcelain cups and pitchers. Now and then it howled a ghostly "hiiip, hiiip," whenever the evening wind blew through the hollow tiles lying about and was turned back by the still standing garden wall.

As if animated by a sudden light, Dr. Nagai came out of his daydream. Quickly he stooped over to dig in the warm ashes with his cane. Pieces of porcelain showed where the kitchen once was. He uncovered a dented, ash-white pan. If these things could talk, they would have broken out into a hymn of immortal conjugal love. Beside them lay a black charred skeleton. The one hand, which had been moving tirelessly up to the very end, lay stiff but was outstretched as if still ready to work beside the ruins of the hearth. The other hand, which had been folded in prayer up till the last breath of air, was still wound around the soot-covered chain with the burned crucifix—

97

her rosary. He who sweated blood for us, was scourged, and crowned with thorns; He who bore the heavy cross and was crucified for us, shed His light upon the mystery of suffering and death for two of His children.

With the finely sensitive hands of a physician, Dr. Nagai carefully bedded the blackened bones of Midori in a white, ash-crusted pail. He did it tenderly and reverently, as if he would be able to fulfill his wife's last request with these gestures, and lighten her dying agony. Then he pressed the vessel firmly and gently to his breast, as if he were carrying the reliquary of some martyr of our modern days. With this holy burden he spent the night in an air raid trench.

Early on the gray morning of August 12 the husband bore his wife to her grave. He climbed with her over the skeletons of the neighbors. Their bones began to shine under the rising tropical sun; they started to move as he walked over them, and seemed to want to say, "Thank you, Midori, for every service you have shown us, and for the example of the life you lived with us."

He carried her past the ash-covered straw-roofed huts of the poor, and half-naked orphan children waved with their little hands, "May God repay your wife, Doctor, for everything she did for us in the Women's Society."

Dr. Nagai crossed near the mouldering wall of the Hongochi Monastery with his burden, past its wonder-working image of the Madonna. The smiling, intact statue seemed to say, "Midori, your secret pilgrimages, early in the morning, are over. Paul, your husband, is saved for a few short years at the price of your life."

He crossed with her through the courtyard of the university where Midori once taught. If the young girls in the cellar shelter had any idea of what was going on, they would have rushed out to escort her to her grave, praying, "God, reward her for the example of her simple, womanly being."

He climbed up the great open crater in the asphalt, and hurried by with her through the ionized air currents of that field of death, paying no attention to the danger. Without being conscious of it, he had sunk into a conversation with her. "Forgive me; forgive me, that I—distracted —so often forgot you. That I became famous and you stayed forgotten at the hearth of our little house. That I helped others first and was not there to die beside you."

Then the husband, buried in his thoughts, stumbled over the roots of a pine tree. The ashes in his arms shook and rustled, and it seemed to him that they were whispering into his ears, "I forgive you. Forgive me, too, that I cannot show you the last services, myself, with my own hands."

On the spot where a pine tree had stood in the cemetery before that day of horror, Dr. Nagai chose a martyr's grave for Midori. The glowing remains of the vanished cathedral's two towers cast their light from the distance on the quiet grave. If the church had not been destroyed, then the priest would be standing at the high altar in red vestments this morning, praying the Epistle from the Mass of the martyrs.

"The souls of the just are in the hands of God

. . . in peace. Even though they suffered hardships at the hands of men . . . God has proved
them. . . . Like gold in the furnace He has tried
them. . . . Like a holocaust He has accepted
them."

VIII

General Chief of Staff without Uniform

After the burial of his wife Dr. Nagai left the smoke-choked blackness of Urakami. Like Abraham he wandered away from the hard-punished city, and puffed up the steep footpath to Koba with a little group of assistants and Sisters of the sick. How long the four miles seemed today! At every tenth step he stopped, put his arm around the shoulders of one of his companions, and heaved a deep sigh of relief. A breeze, fresh with dew, blew down the slope, carrying with it a fine, sharp aroma of pine needles.

Dr. Nagai groped his way toward the mirror-like

"engawa" of his father-in-law's dwelling. Quietly and timidly he pushed the door open until he could look through it. His little band of assistants and nurses stood beside him. Kayano and Makoto recoiled in fright—they stared at their father with open mouths—the little boy, after the first shock, reached for his sister's arm. A grasshopper flew with a little chirp from the hollow of his hand. Slowly and fearfully they crept and cowered back into the dusk of the house. Their wide open eyes were asking: "Is this papa with the blood-covered bandage on his head? Is this papa so weak that he has to lean on a cane and on Sister's arm?"

"Here, try these once. See how good they are." Father Nagai broke the silence and handed them a few peaches from the blackened box he had dug out of the ashes of his home. But the fidgeting fingers of his children were suddenly frozen stiff.

"Why don't you eat them? Why not?" their father demanded, tired and irritated. In answer

103

they broke out into a loud burst of tears. A mother's love and kindness were not to be replaced; there could be no substitute for them.

That same day his duty yet called him on. He took leave of his children. A sharp aroma of medicine stayed behind him in the house. At Fujino-o, five miles from Nagasaki, he rented a house and opened a medical station. Here where a centuries-old mineral spring danced up from the ground at the foot of three mountains, he sought to cool and heal the fiery wounds of the atom victims. First he took a refreshing bath in the nearby mountain stream, washed out his blood-stained clothing in the flowing water, and let it dry in the sun on the rocks. Then he noticed that the right side of his body was all scratched from bits of glass. In the shade of the woods he and his medical staff caught a few hours of sleep after laboring through the night.

* * *

A little troop of dispersed soldiers from a wiped-out company made its way over the hilly land.

The lead man in that failing column had tied up his bleeding head with a threadbare handkerchief. His comrade on the left was limping along with a stiff knee. One of the soldiers in the next row was coughing like an asthmatic old man; the other felt his nearsighted way along, half blind without his glasses. All of them were leaning on creaking canes or walking hand in hand. Shoes and rubber boots had been torn to shreds, and the torn ends of their shirts fluttered behind them. Heads and shoulders were covered with long palm leaves, carefully camouflaged.

"A hunter!" warned a hoarse voice, as the plane swooped above them, to their right. "Watch out for the medicine bottles!" The whole column would drop into the dusty grass or hide behind clusters of rock.

"Forward!" the next command would come after a few minutes, "faster, faster!"

So it went the whole day long: up a hill under the burning sun, then down again into a boxed-off valley at a maddeningly slow pace; into every little village, down into the last hamlet.

Dr. Nagai was the commandant of these expeditions. He set out every morning from his "headquarters" in those last days of August with his "general staff." He knocked on every door, looked behind every block of stone, crawled into every emergency hut, and called after the wounded, the evacuated, the refugees. Like ministering angels, his nurses would unlace the haversacks, take out the bandages, tape, needles.

First they would take off the filthy emergency bandages without a grimace, lift the ugly glass and cement splinters out of the festering wounds, wash, sew, and bandage. They were happy when they could let their patients go with a good-natured jest after sewing up twelve wounds, or when they could encourage them with a "Sasaki gambare" if they found up to a hundred glass splinters in their backs.

"Let's leave these lonely straw huts up here on the top of the hill," Dr. Nagai excused himself one day. Then he plucked up his courage, bundled the last of his failing strength together, and stumbled wearily down the hill. A weak handshake from the dying, or, occasionally, a little cup of tea from their families were his thanks for this selfless love of his neighbors. If all went well, these good Samaritans, silent because they were too weary to speak, would find their way to some shelter in the evening.

They carried their chief homewards on their backs part of the way, and set him down for a brief rest in a farm house. Squatting together on the floor, they tore into the big meal of rice and potatoes like starved dogs. After eating, they struck up once more the carefree conversation of inseparable friendship. They moved closer to each other, talked over the cases they had treated. And then, in the flickering glow of an oil lamp, they joined in a common prayer for the dead workers who had left their ranks. Then they set out on the last part of the journey.

* * *

107

On August 15, Our Lady's Feast Day, Dr. Nagai attended Mass at the little church at Koba. If only Midori and the children could have been at his side! She was always so happy on this day and would have prepared the festival cakes. For August 15 is a happy day of memorial in Japan, the day that Francis Xavier, in 1549, first brought the Gospel of Christ to the dragon-shaped island.

Fiii—Fiii! hissed through the Church window. An American fighter plane was whistling over Koba. The faithful looked for cover. Father Shimizu interrupted the Holy Sacrifice of the Mass and rushed to the door with the Blessed Sacrament in the chalice, hiding near the camellia tree beside his little church.

"The way it looks, the war is over," announced the doctor's assistant, Choro, that evening in an excited tone of voice. He had just come from Nagasaki with medical supplies and groceries, and let the knapsack full of rice, soybean flour, and canned goods slide heavily to the floor.

"How's that? Over?" Dr. Nagai was surprised.

108

"Yes. Unconditional surrender. Complete acceptance of the Potsdam Declaration."

"But—that's impossible," Dr. Nagai protested. "The whole city is beside itself. Some are saying yes, others no. The police are racing through the whole town in their autos shouting, 'We are fighting to the end, even on our own soil!' "

"Doubtless—a bomb—a delayed atom bomb! In a moment it will go off—no one knows that it will explode here—except me—I must destroy it —here, with this bamboo cane—I, I hesitate— now, now it's blowing up—what an awful noise— what a lightning flash!"

"Doctor! Doctor! What's wrong with you?" soothed Sister Superior Fève, bending over Dr. Nagai. "You have a fever," she said softly and laid a damp cloth on his forehead. He braced his arms in order to raise himself.

"Impossible. But it's no wonder," the Sister sighed. "All your wounds have begun to fester. Why? How come you didn't tell us anything about them?"

"It's wartime, an emergency!" the doctor-patient pushed off her reproach, received an injection, and spent the rest of the day alone at the station.

"Doctor," hissed a highly excited voice. Slowly and very sadly the Superior placed a newspaper before Dr. Nagai's eyes. He took it in his hand. A fleeting glance at it was enough; he knew everything. The title said it all: "Imperial Decision Ends War! Japan Is Conquered!"

Stretched out on the floor beside the Superior, the doctor cried like a little child, his shoulders quivering convulsively. Toward evening his helpers returned. When their eyes fell on their leader, they all began to weep.

The tea went untouched. They sat there with their arms folded. The sun went down. The moon rose over the mountains. Not a word was spoken. All were dipping deeply into an ocean of sorrow, until sleep overcame them all.

A new day, August 17, dawned cloudlessly over hilly Fujino-o. But the doctor and his staff had bolted shut their little house in protest against every spark of sunlight. They too had capitulated, given up. The only business they set for themselves now was to spend one whole day doing nothing, for the first time in years.

"Doctor! A patient." A giant peasant was at the door.

"What difference does one more sick man make?" complained the assistant.

"When a hundred million are crying," a Sister added, and with a strong shove she forced the man out through the narrow door slit. Disappointed, he crossed the millet field.

Dr. Nagai's eyes followed him. "Have that man brought back," he commanded the astonished Sister Fève. "Yes, have him brought back," he repeated, as she stood there dumb with surprise. "It is our duty to save men's lives. Our country is conquered, but the wounded still live. The war is over, but our labor of love goes on."

Joy and sacrifice, the demands of his profession

111

shone once more from his gleaming eyes. A violent shiver ran through him from head to foot. His wasted body belonged to the grave, but his soul and spirit were still with his stricken fellow mortals. He buckled on his emergency kit. All the rest imitated him and went out once again on their visits of mercy, caring for the sick.

Whole processions of anxious women and men met them, carrying their chicken coops and their rolled-up quilts away, fleeing from the "invading Americans." "Look, I'm losing my hair!"—"I've lost the color in my face; I look like an unripe melon."—"I'm shivering with fever."—"Where did I get these rusty brown blood blisters on my fingers?" One after another, they brought their complaints to the headquarters in Fujino-o. From seriously sick men they developed into deathly sick men. During the day they were busy caring for others, and at night they tried to cure themselves. They passed out vitamin tablets, and toward evening they took some serum to make themselves sleep.

*   *   *

For a whole week now Dr. Nagai had been shaking with fever. Crisis followed upon crisis. On September 20 his colleagues whispered to one another, "Hopeless! I have given up on him." Just that afternoon a woman knocked at the door, her eyes red from weeping, her "getas" all worn out. "Please! Hurry! My husband! He's at his last gasp!"

Dr. Nagai got up like some one who walks into the face of a living death. In the temporary monastery of Juashin in Kawadoko he stopped to catch his breath, and the Father Abbot flooded him with reproaches. At the last second he reached the dying man on the ridge of the hill. Then he returned home to die himself.

Someone waited for him in his room.

"Dr. Tomita? My pupil? Back from the front? Impossible!"

"That's who I am," he smiled at his teacher.

"But that's wonderful—of you—to have come— from so far," the deathly sick man stretched out his hand slowly. The head Sister from the Marine Hospital gave him an injection and encouraged him, "Now, very quiet, Doctor. Very quiet. You'll get over it."

"Where is Dr. Shi?—Dr. Shi?" he worried, and sank into a dark black unconsciousness. That afternoon he opened his eyes. All his friends were standing around him, encouraging him with their kindly looks. The specialists had been summoned by Dr. Shi. Father Togawa gave him Extreme Unction. The last crisis was upon him.

Through the open windows the three mountains shone in upon the sick man like a symbol of the Blessed Trinity. He repeated twice, half delirious, a little verse of poetry. "The fall clouds disappeared—disappeared—in the clear sky,"—and he knew nothing further.

After a week he woke up. Once again he was saved. Everyone was talking about a miracle. Kayano tried to explain, "My brother and I were praying our rosaries for him constantly, and that's why he got well."

114

IX

Millionaires in Metal Barracks

"Doctor! You're straining the last thread of your health to the breaking point. For seven years all life there will be impossible," the worried Sisters caring for him prophesied. They shook their heads with their little coifs determinedly, and tried to entreat their leader, to influence him, to make him change his mind. But it was no use!

Three weeks after the bombing, Dr. Nagai saw ants swarming over the dust hills; a week later, night crawlers and shaggy, matted rats. And now yellow spotted caterpillars were returning in a regular procession.

"Men can live here too," the professor concluded. "And I shall be the first to prove it." On October 16, he put aside his "command," dismissed his "general staff," and closed his "headquarters" at Fujino-o. He had seen the wounded through the worst at the time of their greatest need.

Midori's relatives built him a new dwelling two thousand feet from the explosion. Perfect! The east wall of the house had remained intact after the bombing. "Two blackened beams on top of it, a few buried sheets of metal on top of that, a corrugated sheet of iron on both the north and south sides, and the paper door at the west front," planned the architects. The researcher had a roof over his head once again. A couple of iron hooks held the walls of the house together, and wadded pieces of paper served as mortar to stop up the holes and cracks. In the clear night the moon shimmered softly and comfortably into the one-room dwelling and took the place of an electric lamp. The approaching winter let a few icicles grow through the wall of the house. Nine persons in the two families moved even closer together in their ten-by-ten room. "It's crowded, but wonderfully warm," bragged the ten-year-old Makoto. But Kayano had a different idea, "Yes, it's warm; but when we sleep, you always kick me, and that hurts!"

The whistling winter storms from the bay always woke the sleepers in their drab gray blankets. Every morning the first duty of the occupants was house cleaning. The pieces of paper that had fallen down had to be pasted and glued back into place once more. Remarkably, no one had had an attack of rheumatism or an inflammation of the lungs. A cup of Japanese tea, their national medicine, was always boiling in a dented kettle on the hearth. A green bottle with its neck broken off served as a water boiler.

The two children had to watch the glowing little fire on the hearth with hawk's eyes as their biggest fortune. When a quick blast of air let the dancing fire die, the neighbor lady would come over to help them with a crackling log. Four-year-old Kayano held her hands together over her head, full of glee, then began to play once more with the doll that her father had made for her out of an old wine bottle.

* * *

During the emergency the medical faculty was divided into three sections. Schoolhouses near the neighboring town of Omoura were pressed into service as hospitals. Dr. Nagai sailed back to Nagasaki with the university students. Now the professor of radiology had to rush here and there for his lectures, climb wearily over mountains of ruins with his cane, and without being able to die, last out a living martyrdom. A temporary hospital at which he gave most of his lectures made him the friendly offer of a room. But to no avail; he refused. "I cannot leave Urakami. I want to rebuild with the people there. Shall I move into this fine lodging while all the others are living in metal barracks? Just look. There and there— houses are rising. What a joy it is for me to see how our city is being built up once more!"

With the trained eye of a research man he saw

life in many new forms in the deserted ruins. Tender grains of wheat sprouted up between the maze of twisted iron and broken tiles, together with bushy ferns and tall potato plants. Even a lonesome morning glory came up, as if to tell, in her blue magnificence, of the goodness of God.

Like an archaeologist, Dr. Nagai climbed over the hills of rubbish in his free hours toward evening, and with the help of one of his children continued digging in the charred remains of his house. He found the golden Order of the Eagle and the highly esteemed medal with the rising sun. They were an ugly black now, horrid and full of holes. So pass the honors of this world. An instructor and three of his advanced students offered their services, helping the sick X-ray researcher.

"What's the idea? Away with that shapeless piece of metal from your melted iron. Throw out the fly wheel from the sewing machine there," the instructor decided. Dr. Nagai could hardly hold back his tears. How unfair it all was to Midori. Now he put his hand quickly into the pocket of the sailor suit they gave him . . . he said to himself, "No longer shall I dig around in these graves. It's breaking my heart. Besides, I've found it!" He was sad and yet happy with archaeologist's joy of discovery. He looked right past a former friend, who walked by slowly with his knapsack, looking in vain for his wife and children and house, murmuring softly to himself.

At home in his little hut, the doctor wiped a handful of dust from a notched hole in the wall. He had already opened up an altar niche and he decorated it with the precious relic from the time of the persecutions under Tokugawa. The bronze body of Christ from the house altar of his destroyed home had miraculously remained intact.

"Everything has been taken from me; this crucifix alone I have managed to find. With my crucifix on the wall I need no more. Praying for my benefactors, I feel I am the richest man on earth. Really! I am a millionaire." With these words he dedicated his little shrine. And very soon he

120

enlarged it and gave the Madonna a place of honor, too.

*   *   *

"Why, look here," Dr. Nagai's sister was telling him, as she pushed away the wobbly wooden frame of a door before the entrance of the den one day. "Why, you can't imagine how I've been looking all over for you, every place I could imagine. Where were you hiding? It's you all right, but you're no bigger than a little mole." She threw herself down at his side with a burst of tears, and did not know whom to pity more, her deathly sick brother, or her dead husband.

"My dearest! But take that heavy knapsack off your back first," Dr. Nagai soothed. She did, and took a long, slender wall clock, wrapped in canvas, from the bag. She placed it on the crooked wall and wound it up with a rusty key. Every tick of the old timepiece, which had once stood at the doctor's house in Izumo, brought back an old childhood memory to the brother and sister. "Truly! Now I have become a millionaire!" Dr. Nagai said gratefully.

More and more often now, however, he had to drop his lectures for a day of rest. Dr. Nagai lay beside the crackling fire wrapped in blankets, his skeleton-like body weak and wet with perspiration. The paper door creaked open to let in a strong gust of wind, and he pulled the covers up closer to his chin. Ichitaro Yamada walked in heavily. He was dressed in a tattered, shot-up soldier's uniform, grumbling and despairing, and contemplating suicide!

"I have nothing more to live for," he whined. "I've heard them call the atom bomb a revenge from heaven. I suppose all the dead were criminals?"

"Please—I am of a different opinion. It was Divine Providence. Let us be thankful for it," Dr. Nagai answered.

"Thankful? Indeed!"

"Yes; look here. This is the rough copy of my address for the memorial services the day after tomorrow. Would you care to read it?"

Yamada took a place in the corner of the room and began to read the prepared speech by the faint light coming through the wadded paper in a crack in the wall, first in a high voice, then in a deep bass, distinctly now and without distress.

"On August 9, 1945, there was a council of war in the imperial headquarters . . . discussing capitulation or . . . at 1202 the bomb burst down upon Urakami . . . 8000 Catholics . . . in one second called before God's judgment throne."

"Summoned before the throne of God," Yamada repeated bitterly and read on.

"August 15 is set aside as the day of peace for the whole world . . . the Feast of the Assumption, the anniversary of our cathedral . . . is that fate or the paternal will of God? . . . Nagasaki was an alternate city, not a primary target for the pilots . . . it was Providence that guided the bomb here . . . through unfavorable and yet favorable winds . . . Catholic and consecrated Urakami was chosen and privileged

123

to burn on the altar of expiation for the war-time crimes of the Second World War . . . other cities were destroyed . . . but they were not acceptable before God . . . Urakami with the church that kept pure the Faith for 400 years . . . and always prayed for peace in every war . . . pleased Him as a victim, and He was appeased. How grand and wondrous, how beautiful and noble! Her 8000 Catholics . . . how fortunate, how spotless they stand before their Lord! . . . and our lot, how terrible it is! . . . why are we still alive? Because there has been too much sin, and too little reparation . . . here, this time, this is our day of propitiation and penance . . . in hunger and thirst, in sweat and sorrow . . . and He will help us, He Who carried His cross to Calvary, Christ Jesus our Lord!"

Ichitaro Yamada choked. A tear shone on his leathery cheek. "God gives and God takes. Praised be His Name! Let us thank Him. Urakami was chosen for this sacrifice. Let us praise Him. This sorrow has made possible the peace of the world." Yamada closed his eyes. After a few seconds he said, as if in prayer, "My wife and children are not in hell. But what of us, we who are still here?"

"We have not yet passed the test to enter into heaven," answered Dr. Nagai.

"Failed our test? Yes, that's it—failed our test." Both men smiled. Yamada rose and said, "I'll work to find my wife once more in heaven!"

Dr. Nagai nodded his head and added, "Good! Let's begin right now. Let's build up this atomic waste once more, amid tears and tireless energy."

*   *   *

On All Souls' Day a Pontifical Requiem was celebrated on the location of the cathedral for the 8000 dead of the Catholic congregation. Bishops in their splendid purple capes, priests in their simple cotton cassocks, and nuns in their gray habits stood in a semi-circle about the place of sacrifice. Before them the relatives of the deceased stretched 8000 white candles into an immense cross for the altar.

125

When they all joined to sing the "De profundis," their voices choked. After the Holy Sacrifice offered for the dead, the bomb-torn streets in the direction of the cemetery became an immense way of the cross for the many who were following after their Lord. Those who were left behind planted the sign of the Crucified over the ashes of their loved ones in the graveyard. Kayano followed the example of his elders. On the crossbeam of his monument was written, "Midori Nagai."

* * *

The Christmas Vigil of that sorrow-filled year dawned at last. It was welcome—after the many Masses for the dead during the month of the poor souls. A small group of young people were taking an evening stroll, walking past the bomb craters and the hills of rubble. At the ruins of the cathedral they bent down over the mounded red stones. They were looking for gold. Dr. Nagai leaned heavily on his cane, panting and watching. That evening he discovered the theme of a sensational book which he would live to write in his little den.

"It's buried right here," Yamada pointed. They had fashioned a winch on what was once the choir of the cathedral. Something shining was moving down in the dust. A chain was around it. The mouldering masonry began to give. The chain was straining. In the ruddy late afternoon sky the little bell of Nagasaki rose from the rubble. "It has gold in it. That's why it was spared, when the bigger one alongside it was melted in the heat," parents explained to their children.

One of the young men played sexton and made the bell sing with a blow from an iron bar. They all fell on their knees. Yamada began, "The Angel of the Lord declared unto Mary. . ."

X

The First Citizen of Japan

"To Nyokodo? Why, yes! To Nyokodo in Nagasaki. That's where we'll have our school outing," decided the teachers.

"And Nyokodo? Why, of course! You must have seen Nyokodo," explained the tourist to the visitors of Nagasaki.

To Nyokodo the missionaries went when they passed through Nagasaki and had to wait for the next steamer.

At Nyokodo the purple-clad hierarchy stopped, and their silken cassocks rustled on the narrow doorposts.

Nyokodo was a poor little wooden house, a spiritual center of Japan, a one-room emergency barracks, the focus of the four islands of Japan, the quarters of Dr. Nagai, a magnet for his fellow citizens since 1947.

Friendly carpenters had donated a new refuge to the atom-sick scientist on the location of the former cathedral, hard by the temporary church of Urakami. In the middle of the rubble in a little flower garden behind a bamboo fence there rose a new cottage with a tile roof.

Beaming and weeping for joy, Dr. Nagai christened the "palace" Nyokodo, which means: "Love your neighbor as yourself." He could be seen there with his cane in his hand making plans and suggestions as they furnished his residence. "Here, lay the quilts and pillows for my sick and deathbed flat on the floor in the middle. And beside it the little varnished table with my writing implements handy. How thoughtful of the workmen! My writing table is already there. Please, may I lay this manuscript on it, "The Bells of

129

Nagasaki"? Look! The little house altar is combined with the bookstand. Perhaps one more bench for visitors, if I may be so bold?"

* * *

When the spring of 1947 moved into the peninsula of Hisen with its gay and happy songs and colors, Dr. Nagai lay down at long last on his four years' sickbed in the "house of brotherly love." The Sisters from the disbanded X-ray institute took turns nursing him. How weak and helpless their energetic chief had become! His athletic figure had wasted away to a thin skeleton, and the lower part of his body was puffed out of shape with his swollen spleen and liver. He had to barricade himself behind tall medicine chests against the loving, mischievous, surprise visits of his children.

Promoted to form-master only two semesters ago, he was already forced to give up his professor's chair, his title, and his salary. What would he live on in these last and most fearful days of his life? Where would he find the school tuition each month for Makoto at the Marianist Brothers and Kayano with the Ursulines?

The scientist did not despair—he had a solution. "My head can still work. My eyes, my ears, my hands, my fingers—they are still good. I can write."

Stretched out on his back, Dr. Nagai began writing on a drawing board with a thin pencil. As soon as his wasted arms grew tired from the effort, the children had to massage them. Every time his straining head grew weary and heavy as lead, the nurse had to bring him a cup of strong coffee.

In "Rosario no Kusari," "The Rosary Chain," he painted an undying monument to Midori. But the manuscript, which he had written almost with blood and tears, and certainly suffering with fever, came back from every publishing house as literary waste paper, always with the observation, "Useless scribbling by a specialist."

Then Dr. Shikiba, a physician and publisher in Tokyo, got hold of the manuscript. On the morning "The Rosary Chain" appeared, all copies were bought up. The fight for his autobiography in 1949 and for his principal work, "The Bells of Nagasaki," which the censors of the provisional government had just released, was even greater.

One book after another left the little room at Nyokodo now. In four years the total ran to twenty volumes, five of which were best sellers in Japan. His fatherly will to his children, Makoto and Kayano, was bought by 220,000 readers in just one year. Dr. Nagai became in actual fact one of the best-known men in Japan.

A man marked with the stamp of death was doing a herculean work for the moral and spiritual reconstruction of his fatherland.

A man wounded in war was working a small miracle for the peace of the world.

A sick layman was a successful missionary, and conquered unnumbered heathens for the Church. Even the Buddhist monks behind their monastery walls bowed with reverence before Dr. Nagai.

132

A movie director, with the most modern equipment in his trunks, dared to knock at the wobbly door of Nyokodo, and begged until Dr. Nagai let him have the motion picture rights. A group of actors, of whom only a few were Catholics, filmed "The Bells of Nagasaki," and some 100,000 movie goers throughout the land were touched to tears, while many hundreds were converted.

Dr. Nagai could have been well on the way toward becoming enormously rich. But he chose instead to find his riches in poverty, in good deeds. He established a library for children alongside his house, and gave two million yen for building churches and schools. This was almost the full total of the royalties for the works that had cost him so much effort.

"But wearing yourself out so!" his friends reproached him and shook their heads. They always received a ready answer: "These projects are helping the reconstruction of Japan. For this reconstruction I shall work and pray with joy. Now, when I should be working as much as possible for

133

my country, I find myself tied down to bed. Shouldn't I do anything at all to help her rise to her feet? Should I rather be an added burden upon her, my two children and I?"

Even one month before his death he still could not lay down his pencil. But now his leukemia was eating the last reserves of strength from his muscles. He had to use finer and finer pencils. Then he could write no longer and instead began to paint some fifteen water colors. His subjects were the Mysteries of the Rosary, for the parish church at Urakami. Dr. Nagai would not be idle for a single day of his life.

"This is the famous house of brotherly love. This man is Dr. Nagai. Look at him well," a grade school teacher was nodding and gesticulating to her class. She had posted them inside the house and along the garden fence outside in a double row. The small visitors stood on tiptoe to squint their eyes at him. If they could only have known what the poor sick man was thinking and later wrote about them.

"I had the impression that I was a bear in the zoo. But since I have finally dedicated my whole life to the service of my fellow men, I am glad to be a bear in a zoo or anything else, as long as I can satisfy the children on their outing."

The following day the nurse came early in the morning. She carefully straightened out the black quilt with its white star pattern and blew every bit of dust from the house altar. For today the Bishop Yamaguchi of Nagasaki was scheduled to visit Dr. Nagai, and was to have with him besides the Apostolic Delegate, the Archbishop of Furstenburg.

There was hardly a break for a single day in the processions to the retreat of the atomic sufferer. Nyokodo was a new shrine in the city of pilgrimages. A sick man whispered into the ear of his neighbor, "Have you heard of the penitent in Nagasaki? Go see him! He can help you with his prayers and suffering."

Dr. Nagai was thus a physician once again. With his kindliness he literally smiled the wounds from

135

their hearts. They were always startled to see a sick man before them who, even in raging pain and glowing with fever, was so calm and so completely resigned to the will of God, who dedicated himself so willingly to everyone's need, and who had, in addition to all this, not lost his Christian sense of humor.

On May 29, 1949, banners in the papal colors streamed from the lamp-posts, and arches fluttering with bands of paper were erected in the streets of Nagasaki. Japan was celebrating the four-hundred-year jubilee of the coming of her Apostle, that great soldier of Christ, Francis Xavier. To honor the Catholics, the Emperor planted a little tree with his own hand beside the monument of the Saint in Nagasaki.

The patient of Nyokodo was carried on a swaying litter through the falling rain from the Mass altar to the cathedral square. A silver reliquary had been brought from the Eternal City by airplane. As a dying man, Dr. Nagai wanted to kiss and venerate the remains of the arm of that great missionary who died on Sanzian.

The visit marked the last time that Dr. Nagai left his sickbed.

A month later, on June 28th, when the nurse visited Dr. Nagai, it was clear that death was at hand. The door opened and His Highness, the Japanese Emperor Hirohito, in a modest black civilian suit, stood on the threshold of the little house of brotherly love. A bundle of human misery and pain lay before him on the floor. This was Dr. Nagai, the scientist, the most powerful minister in his own way of the empire. His Highness bowed and thanked the doctor. It was a gesture the Emperor performed on behalf of millions throughout the land.

Two days later the ring and cross of a high prince of the Church sparkled in the poor barracks-like room. The Papal Legate, Cardinal Gilroy, from Sydney, Australia, was bringing the blessing for the sick.

On December 23rd of the same year, a sealed box with a gilded document of honor left the Imperial Palace in Tokyo. On the same state-holiday, the Communist ambassadors climbed down the carpet-covered stairs of the parliament building with deep wrinkles in their foreheads and with clenched fists. For the first time in Japanese history, a Catholic had been named a national hero, the first citizen of the empire: Dr. Nagai, who during the time of war "contributed most to the moral and material welfare of the country." On June 1, 1950, Emperor Hirohito, upon the motion of parliament, sent a silver cup to the patient of Urakami, and the Prime Minister sent a finely-done letter with it.

In an imposing audience during the Holy Year of 1950 Pope Pius XII had just spoken to the pilgrims and ambassadors of every part of the world. Then he heard of Dr. Nagai's illness. At a late hour the same night, he dispatched his paternal blessing to his great son in Japan in a personal letter, and sent along a rosary as a personal gift.

Now the city of Nagasaki, too, hastened to add to the accolades. Dr. Nagai was named honorary mayor of Nagasaki—not just honorary citizen.

Dr. Nagai was now rich and esteemed because during his entire life he had been content with the role of a beggar. For example, after the bombing, there were just five yen in the pocket of his warden's uniform, barely enough to buy a post card and tell his relatives of his misfortune. And of a fortune of 100 yen he once received in his emergency dwelling, he gave part of it to a Polish Franciscan as his contribution toward the reconstruction of a monastery, traded the rest of it for a Bible and a little statue of the Blessed Virgin. His son remarked of all the honors and titles, "My father will not stand for it."

*   *   *

The spring month of March, 1951, spread its cloudless skies over Nagasaki. From the distant peak of the lordly Mount Aso black patches of rock showed through the melting snow. In the garden at Nyokodo, the first sprouts of the spring flowers were peeping above the ground. But inside the house of brotherly love a man was slowly dying, piece by piece. His white corpuscle count mounted to an abnormal 330,000. The patient was made tired and listless even by the lightest handshake. Sleep seemed to hover ever far away, his asthma choked him and clutched after his heart.

Dr. Nagai would no longer let the rosary, the fatherly gift of Pius XII, from his hand. During the long, sleepless nights he counted the passing hours by the rosaries he recited. After each Ave he added, "Heiwa-wo—give us peace." From time to time he took his little brush from the sick table together with a piece of paper no bigger than his open hand. Slowly he would paint "Heiwa-wo" on it, press "Poro Nagai" beneath it in dark red letters with a little stamp, and pass the sheets out among his friends. Altogether he made more than a thousand copies of this last little greeting.

When Dr. Nagai was asked where he was able to find this last reservoir of apostolic strength, he answered, "The Most Blessed Sacrament, which Father Uschida brings me every Sunday, gives me a most wonderful power. Of myself I can do nothing."

In April of 1951 he had finished his last book, and with it his life's work. Would Makoto continue it? "There is one wish close to my heart," Dr. Nagai wrote once to his son's teacher. "I hope sincerely that he will be an atom researcher. . . . Then I could leave this world in perfect happiness."

On April 30th the dying doctor received the Last Sacraments. He prepared for them through a long night of fever, without allowing himself a single swallow of water for the thirst that tortured him incessantly. As a last token of honor and gratitude his friends brought him to the hospital once more. He gave a father's blessing to his 16-year-old son, who was still studying with the Marianists, and took leave of him forever: "Work and study diligently for our people and for humanity. But above all else try—and this is even greater—to be a priest of God." On the first day of May, the month of the Blessed Virgin, he awoke from his unconsciousness and prayed, "Jesus, Mary, Joseph!" Then, softly, and with a look of transfigured glory, as if in the echo of eternity: "Waga tamashi wo witeni makase tate-

matsuru—Into your hands I commend my spirit."
Makoto pressed the cross and the relics from the
times of the persecution into his hands. "Pray
. . . Pray," were his last words; then his heart
was still. He was only 43 years of age. The transfigured smile of a saint remained on his dead
features.

* * *

Nagasaki prepared for the pomp of his funeral
on May 3rd. The mayor of the city headed the
funeral procession. Poro's two orphans walked
behind the coffin. The Bishop of Nagasaki was
celebrant at the Pontifical Requiem Mass. Tens
of thousands of the faithful crowded about the
temporary wooden church in Urakami. . . .
After the Mass, the Primate of Japan blessed
the last remains of the great and patient sufferer.
Makoto and Kayano sprinkled the coffin with
holy water. Then the bells of all the towers in
the whole city took up the lamentation for the
dead.

In the Buddhist monasteries the monks pushed

the mighty beams against the cup-shaped temple bells with a heavy clang. The sirens were howling from the factories and from the ships in the bay. An immense crowd of people formed a three-mile-long funeral cortege to the cemetery where Midori and the other victims of the atom bomb were resting.

Pedestrians stopped to watch in awe and respect. Workers put aside their work. The motor vehicles, all the traffic on the streets, were quiet. Everyone prayed for the great citizen who had now departed.

The Holy Father wept for this great son of the Church and sent his condolences to the Japanese nation. Prime Minister Yoshida and President Amano of the Board of Education sent telegrams of sympathy. All of the newspapers, even the Buddhist publications, paid tribute to the life and death of Dr. Nagai in lengthy columns, calling him the "Saint of the Atom Bomb."

Yet it was as if Dr. Nagai sought to ward off all this recognition. He asked them to put this inscription on his grave stone: "I was but a humble servant. I have but done my duty."

Part of his will read: "I am grateful to the atom bomb; it has led me to God."

A NOTE ON THE TYPE

IN WHICH THIS BOOK IS SET

This book is set in Vogue, an Intertype face, patterned after the original sans serif design credited to Paul Renner, a German architect who became devoted to letter design and typography. Vogue is devoid of subtle insincerity. Simple geometrical elements express its utter frankness. Characters leap to the eye unconfused by decoration, needing no ornamental crutches. It is a smart, fresh type face of extreme simplicity. The book was composed and printed by the York Composition Company, Inc., of York, Pa., and bound by Moore and Company of Baltimore. The typography and design by Howard N. King.